Test Bank

Charles M. Byles
Virginia Commonwealth University

International Management: Managing Across Borders and Cultures
Sixth Edition

Helen Deresky

Upper Saddle River, New Jersey 07458

Editor-in-Chief: David Parker
Product Development Manager: Ashley Santora
Production Editor: Kevin Holm
Buyer: Arnold Vila

Pearson Prentice Hall[TM] **is a trademark of Pearson Education, Inc.**

10 9 8 7 6 5 4 3 2 1

ISBN-13: 978-0-13-614329-1
ISBN-10:   0-13-614329-6

Contents

PREFACE

Welcome to the Test Bank for Helen Deresky's *International Management: Managing Across Borders and Culture*, Sixth Edition. The test bank has been carefully revised for the new edition, and contains questions that cover the major topics of each chapter. The questions allow the instructor to assess the student's knowledge and understanding of both the conceptual material and the applications contained in the Opening Profile, Management Focus, and Comparative Management in Focus sections in the chapter. A large number of questions are provided with many choices so that the instructor can easily construct a 50 or 75 minute exam over several chapters. For each chapter, there are enough choices for a test on that chapter alone. A number of questions are deliberately repetitive in order to give the instructor more flexibility. Some instructors have found it useful to assign odd-numbered questions as a study guide while reserving some of the even-numbered questions for the actual test.

The questions follow a logical sequence from the beginning to end of the chapter. Questions that have application content, or are based on examples from the textbook, or may be a little integrative in nature are marked with an asterisk in the answer choice.

The correct answers to questions are in bold font, with the difficulty level and page number where the material is covered in the textbook contained in parentheses.

New to this edition! **AACSB Learning Standards Tags**

 What is the AACSB?

AACSB is a not-for-profit corporation of educational institutions, corporations and other organizations devoted to the promotion and improvement of higher education in business administration and accounting. A collegiate institution offering degrees in business administration or accounting may volunteer for AACSB accreditation review. The AACSB makes initial accreditation decisions and conducts periodic reviews to promote continuous quality improvement in management education. Pearson Education is a proud member of the AACSB and is pleased to provide advice to help you apply AACSB Learning Standards.

What are AACSB Learning Standards?

One of the criteria for AACSB accreditation is the quality of the curricula. Although no specific courses are required, the AACSB expects a curriculum to include learning experiences in such areas as:

- **Communication**
- **Ethical Reasoning**
- **Analytic Skills**
- **Use of Information Technology**
- **Multicultural and Diversity**
- **Reflective Thinking**

These six categories are AACSB Learning Standards. Questions that test skills relevant to these standards are tagged with the appropriate standard. For example, a question testing the moral questions associated with externalities would receive the Ethical Reasoning tag.

How can I use these tags?

Tagged questions help you measure whether students are grasping the course content that aligns with AACSB guidelines noted above. In addition, the tagged questions may help to identify potential applications of these skills. This in turn may suggest enrichment activities or other educational experiences to help students achieve these goals.

This edition also assigns one or more AACSB categories (Global, Ethics, Technology, Communication, and Diversity) to each question.

I hope that the test bank will serve as an integral part of the learning and assessment process for your students. If you have any comments or questions, please let me know.

Best wishes.

Charles M. Byles
Department of Management
Virginia Commonwealth University
Richmond, Virginia
Tel: 804-828-7125
cmbyles@vcu.edu
October 18, 2007

Chapter 1
Assessing the Environment
Political, Economic, Legal, Technological

Multiple Choice Questions

1. The term globalism or globalization generally refers to _____.
    a. increasing loyalty to your own country
    b. global competition characterized by networks that bind countries, institutions, and people.
    c. competition in an increasingly borderless world
    d. b and c only (easy, page 4)

2. Which of the following is correct about measuring globalization:
    a. The United States is the most globalized country.
    b. Globalization is measured using only economic factors.
    c. Trade, travel, technology, and links with the rest of the world are four comprehensive measures of globalization. (easy, page 5)
    d. The United States leads all countries in trade, travel, and links with the rest of the world.

3. The hostility to the takeover of Europe's largest steel company, Acelor, by India's Mittal Steel illustrates
    a. the decrease in nationalism and increase in globalism.
    b. the backlash against globalism. (moderate, page 6)
    c. the decline in competitiveness in the steel industry.
    d. cultural differences about the benefits of takeovers.

4. Small and medium-sized enterprises (SMEs)
    a. are generally not competing internationally.
    b. are major investors in world markets.
    c. face good opportunities currently as a result of trade shows, export initiatives, and the Internet. (moderate, page 7)
    d. are unaffected by globalism

5. Gayle Warwick Fine Linen owes its success primarily to _____.
    a. a large dedicated staff in England
    b. the ability to source embroiderers and skilled craftspeople in Vietnam (moderate, page 7)*
    c. the fact that she speaks French fluently
    d. all of the above

6. The three major world currencies today are _____.
   a. **euro, yen, U.S. dollar (easy, page 8)**
   b. euro, yen, peso
   c. euro, U.S. dollar, German mark
   d. euro, U.S. dollar, peso

7. In which of the following three regional free-trade blocs does most of today's world trade take place?
   a. Western Europe, Eastern Europe, and North America
   b. Western Europe, Asia, and the United States
   c. **Western Europe, Asia, and North America (moderate, page 8)**
   d. Europe, Southeast Asia, and the Americas

8. The European Union currently consists of how many nations?
   a. Ten
   b. **Twenty-seven (easy, page 8)**
   c. Forty
   d. Fifty

9. Which of the following countries is not one of the Four Tigers?
   a. South Korea
   b. Hong Kong
   c. Taiwan
   d. **Thailand (moderate, pages 9)**

10. China has enjoyed recent success as an export powerhouse built upon its _____.
    a. **strengths of low costs and flow of capital (difficult, page 9) {AACSB: Multicultural/Diversity}**
    b. geographic location in the world
    c. high educational standards
    d. close ties with Japan

11. Which of the following statements is **not correct** about China?
    a. China joined the WTO in 2002
    b. **One of China's key strengths is its excellent infrastructure (difficult, page 9) {AACSB: Multicultural/Diversity}**
    c. China is stuck halfway between a command economy and a market economy
    d. China continues to enjoy significant inflows of money from ethnic Chinese outside of China

12. Which of the following statements is **correct** about India?
    a. India's biggest contributor to growth is its excellent infrastructure.
    b. India is the world's leader for outsourced back-office services, and increasingly for high tech services
    c. India is the fastest-growing free-market democracy
    d. b and c only are correct (difficult, page 9)

13. India is slowly making a name not just for software exports and service outsourcing, but also as an exporter of
    a. wine
    b. autos, auto parts, and motorcycles (moderate, page 14)*
    c. chemicals, and chemical processing equipment
    d. glass and mirrors

14. India's economic boom is a result of
    a. reducing protectionism and red tape
    b. lifting restrictions on foreign investment
    c. reforming its financial sectors
    d. all of the above (moderate, page 13)*

15. Which of the following are characteristics of the Mexican trading environment?
    a. Mexican trade policy is among the most open in the world
    b. Trade with the U.S. and Canada has tripled since NAFTA was ratified in 1994
    c. In recent years, almost 85% of Mexico's exports go to the United States
    d. All of the above are characteristics of the Mexican trading environment (difficult, page 10)

16. Which of the following is not correct?
    a. Foreign investors have become wary of Russia because of recent government action against the Yukos oil group.
    b. Africa has been ignored by most of the world's investors
    c. Because of the political and economic risks in LDCs, they offer no potential international business opportunities (difficult, page 11)*
    d. South Africa has the biggest economy in Africa.

17. Of all the developments propelling global business today, the one that is transforming the international managers agenda the most is
    a. information technology (easy, page 14) {AACSB: Use of Information Technology}
    b. political unrest
    c. increased nationalism
    d. ethnic strife

18. What kinds of jobs are currently being offshored/outsourced from the United States of America?
   a. tax processing
   b. factory, production, assembly line jobs
   c. high skilled medical analysis, computer programming jobs
   d. all of the above (easy, page 15)*

19. The U.S is offshoring white-collar computer programming jobs to India because _____.
   a. Indians are better programmers than Americans
   b. Indians speak better English than Americans
   c. Indian programmers cost one-fourth the cost of equivalent American programmers (moderate, page 15)*
   d. all of the above

20. An important aspect of the political environment is the phenomenon of _____ - a driving force behind political instability around the world.
   a. ethnicity (moderate, page 15) {AACSB: Multicultural/Diversity}
   b. government oppression
   c. fascism
   d. racism

21. Political risks are any governmental actions or politically motivated events that adversely affect the _____.
   a. capacity of the company to survive
   b. long-run profitability or value of the company (moderate, page 17)
   c. personal safety of corporate managers and employees
   d. company's capacity to meet consumer needs

22. Which of the following best describes nationalization?
   a. use of locals in management positions
   b. giving hiring precedence to locals over employees from the company's headquarters
   c. government's gradual and subtle actions against a firm
   d. forced sale of an MNC's assets to local buyers (moderate, page 17)

23. _____ occurs when the local government seizes the foreign-owned assets of the MNC and provides inadequate compensation.
   a. Nationalization
   b. Expropriation (easy, page 17)
   c. Confiscation
   d. Repatriation

24. The risk of expropriation is highest in countries that _____.
   a. have a large number of MNCs operating there
   b. experience continuous political upheaval, violence, and change (easy, page 17)
   c. have low levels of education and economic development
   d. have stable economies

25. Suppose the government of Karakozia seizes all assets of Pepsi in Karakozia without offering any compensation to the company. This action on the part of the government is an example of _____.
   a. nationalization
   b. repatriation
   c. expropriation
   d. confiscation (moderate, page 17)*

26. Events that affect all foreign firms doing business in a country or region are called _____.
   a. macro political risk events (easy, page 17)
   b. micro political risk events
   c. country risk events
   d. regional risk events

27. Zagreb Inc., negotiates a multi-million dollar contract with the government to provide electricity to country A. The government is voted out of power shortly after and the new government changes the contract for all oil producing companies. This is an example of _____.
   a. barriers to repatriation
   b. expropriation
   c. confiscation
   d. micro political risk (moderate, page 17)*

28. Foreign governments sometimes inordinately delay granting licenses and permissions to do businesses in their countries- commonly known as "death from a thousand cuts". This is an example of _____.
   a. creeping expropriation (moderate, page 17)*
   b. globalism
   c. barriers to repatriation
   d. confiscation

29. Micro political risk events are those that affect _____.
   a. numerous industries or companies
   b. several other nations in the same region
   c. one industry or company or a few companies (easy, page 17)
   d. managers and employees who are nationals

30. Which of the following is not one of the seven typical political risk events common today?
   a. loss of technology or intellectual property rights
   b. **political takeovers and civil wars (moderate, page 17)**
   c. discriminatory treatment in the application of laws
   d. interference in managerial decision making

31. Expropriation of corporate assets without prompt and adequate compensation is an example of _____.
   a. economic risk
   b. **political risk (easy, page 17)**
   c. legal risk
   d. cultural risk

32. Risk assessment by multinational corporations usually takes two forms: _____ and _____.
   a. use of experts or consultants; newspaper reports
   b. **use of experts or consultants; internal staff (moderate, page 17)**
   c. use of internal staff; publications
   d. government risk reports; computer modeling

33. No matter how sophisticated the methods of political risk assessment become, nothing can replace timely information from _____.
   a. government agencies
   b. broadcast media
   c. academic research
   d. **people on the front line (moderate, page 18)**

34. The key to a PRISM system is the _____.
   a. quantity of data input by executives
   b. number of variables in the PRISM equations
   c. **quality of the data input by executives and consultants (moderate, page 18)***
   d. power of the computers

35. To analyze their data on potential risks, some companies allocate a minimum and a maximum score for which of the following criteria?
   a. the political and economic environment
   b. domestic economic conditions
   c. external economic relations
   d. **all of the answers are correct (difficult, page 18)**

36. All of the following are categories used in political risk assessment *except*_____.
    a. political and economic environment
    b. domestic economic conditions
    c. external economic relations
    d. political elections (moderate, page 18)

37. _____ involves the use of lead indicators to predict possible political dangers such as signs of violence or riots.
    a. Computer modeling system
    b. PRISM
    c. Composite ranking
    d. Early warning system (moderate, page 18)

38. Managers also evaluate the impact of political risk on the company. For autonomous international subsidiaries, most of the impact from political risks will be at the level of _____ in terms of political environment.
    a. ownership and control (moderate, page 18)*
    b. financial operations
    c. marketing and sales operations
    d. managerial strategy and policy-making

39. For global firms, the primary impact is likely to be at the level of _____.
    a. ownership and control
    b. marketing and sales
    c. the firm's transfers (or exchanges) of money, products, or component parts (moderate, page 18)
    d. managerial strategy and policy making

40. Which of the following risk management strategies is <u>not</u> a form of adaptation to the political regulatory environment?
    a. equity sharing
    b. participative management
    c. localization
    d. hedging (difficult, page 19)*

41. Which of the following risk management strategies is <u>not</u> a means of adaptation?
    a. participative management
    b. development assistance
    c. funds sharing (difficult, page 19)*
    d. localization of the operation

42. Which of the following is an example of localization of operations?
    a. modify the subsidiary's name to suit local tastes
    b. change management style to adapt to local culture
    c. advertise its products using local models
    d. **all of the above are examples of localization (moderate, page 19)***

43. When a foreign company initiates a joint venture with a local company as a way of adapting to risk, the foreign company is following a strategy of _____.
    a. **equity sharing (moderate, page 19)***
    b. participative management
    c. localization of the operation
    d. development assistance

44. Which of the following requires that the firm actively involves nationals in the management of the subsidiary?
    a. equity sharing
    b. **participative management (moderate, page 19)**
    c. localization of the operation
    d. development assistance

45. Companies often reduce risk in foreign countries by creating dependency of a subsidiary on the host country. Which of the following is <u>not</u> a means of maintaining dependency?
    a. market control
    b. **equity sharing (difficult, page 19)**
    c. staged contribution strategies
    d. input control

46. _____ means that the firm maintains control over key inputs, such as raw materials, components, technology, and know-how.
    a. **Input control (moderate, page 19)**
    b. Market control
    c. Position control
    d. Bureaucratic control

47. Which of the following requires that the firm keep control of the means of distribution (for example, by only manufacturing components for the parent firm or legally blocking sales outside the host country)?
    a. input control
    b. **market control (moderate, page 19)***
    c. position control
    d. bureaucratic control

48. When a MNC keeps certain key subsidiary management positions in the hands of expatriate or home-office managers, it is exercising _____.
   a. input control
   b. market control
   c. position control (moderate, page 19)
   d. bureaucratic control

49. When GM does not allow its subsidiary company in China that manufactures cars to sell these cars outside China, it is exercising

   _____.
   a. input control
   b. position control
   c. hedging
   d. market control (moderate, page 19)*

50. If a U.S. firm borrows money from a host country bank as a hedge against being forced out of operation without adequate compensation, this method of managing political risk is called _____.
   a. local debt financing (easy, page 19)
   b. position control
   c. development assistance
   d. adaptation

51. Political risk insurance is a form of _____.
   a. input control
   b. development assistance
   c. equity sharing
   d. hedging (difficult, page 19)

52. The Overseas Private Investment Corporation is a _____.
   a. large overseas bank
   b. currency hedging center
   c. provider of political risk insurance (moderate, page 19)
   d. United Nations subsidiary

53. Political risk insurance usually covers _____.
   a. losses in revenues not assets
   b. losses in both revenues and assets
   c. losses in assets but not revenues (moderate, page 19)
   d. none of the answers are correct

54.   Which of the following is a form of hedging?
        a.   staged contribution strategies
        b.   development assistance
        c.   local debt financing (difficult, page 19)
        d.   localization of the operation

55.   The threat of terrorism affects MNCs in _____.
        a.   Middle East
        b.   Latin America
        c.   China
        d.   potentially all over the world including USA (easy, page 19)*

56.   In 2002, foreign firms operating in Argentina faced problems mainly due
        to _____.
        a.   overthrow of previous government
        b.   expropriation of assets
        c.   economic instability (moderate, page 20)*
        d.   riots in the northern region

57.   A country's level of _____ generally determines its economic stability.
        a.   agricultural development
        b.   industrial development
        c.   international debt
        d.   economic development (moderate, page 20)

58.   A country's ability or intention to meet its financial obligations
        determines its _____.
        a.   economic risk (moderate, page 20)
        b.   legal risk
        c.   political risk
        d.   country risk

59.   When the Russian ruble was devalued in 1998, the effect on the Russian
        people was
        a.   imported goods became cheaper.
        b.   imported goods became more expensive (difficult, page 20)*
        c.   Russians were able to purchase more for a given amount of money.
        d.   there was no effect on the purchasing power of Russians

60.   A US based MNC operating in Mexico would be affected if Mexico
        devalues its currency because the _____.
        **a.   MNC would be able to repatriate less profits in dollars
             (moderate, page 20)***
        b.   MNC will have to pay more taxes locally
        c.   MNC will be forced to shut down operations in Mexico
        d.   MNC will have to employ more local labor

61. John Mathis' four recommended methods of analyzing economic risk include all of the following *except* _____.
    a. the quantitative approach
    b. the axiomatic approach (moderate, pages 20-21)
    c. the qualitative approach
    d. the checklist approach

62. Which of the following is not a generally accepted method of assessing the creditworthiness of a country?
    a. quantitative approach
    b. survey approach (moderate, pages 20-21)
    c. qualitative approach
    d. checklist approach

63. The _____ method of analyzing economic risk attempts to measure statistically a country's ability to honor its debt obligation.
    a. quantitative (moderate, page 21)
    b. qualitative
    c. checklist approach
    d. subjective/objective analysis

64. The qualitative approach to economic risk evaluation involves assessing _____ and _____.
    a. a country's resources for payments; its willingness to pay its obligations
    b. the competence of its leaders; analyzing policies they are likely to implement(difficult, page 21)
    c. the probability of terrorism; resources for payments
    d. none of the above

65. Representatives of a MNC seek an interview with local government leaders in the Department of Commerce in India with a view to assess the types of policies likely to be implemented. According to Mathis, this is an example of _____.
    a. qualitative approach (moderate, page 21)*
    b. quantitative approach
    c. checklist approach
    d. a combination of all of the above

66. The _____ approach to analyzing economic risk relies on a few easily measurable and timely criteria believed to reflect or indicate changes in the creditworthiness of the country.
    a. qualitative
    b. checklist (moderate, page 21)
    c. statistical
    d. brainstorming

67. Many foreign companies in China often face losses because _____.
   a. the local government does not stand behind commitments of state-owned enterprises (moderate, page 21)*
   b. the local market is not large enough
   c. the government mandates high wages and benefits to be paid to workers
   d. all of the above

68. The situation faced by Mr. David Ji, the Chinese-American electronics entrepreneur, in his dispute with China's largest television manufacturer illustrates
   a. the sophistication of the Chinese legal system.
   b. protection of powerful Chinese companies by China's judicial system (moderate, page 21)
   c. the use of *guanxi* in resolving a complex problem.
   d. Protections offered to American companies in China.

69. The host country's legal system is derived from _____.
   a. common law
   b. civil law
   c. Islamic law
   d. all of the above (easy, page 22)

70. An international agreement which regulates international business by spelling out the rights and obligations of the seller and buyer is _____.
   a. Universal Contract law
   b. Universal Civil law
   c. Universal Criminal law
   d. United Nations Conventions on Contracts for International Sale of Goods (easy, page 21)

71. Under what form of law are past court decisions used as precedents?
   a. bureaucratic law
   b. civil law
   c. common law (easy, page 22)
   d. cultural law

72. _____ is based on a comprehensive set of laws organized into a code.
   a. Bureaucratic law
   b. Civil law (easy, page 22)
   c. Common law
   d. Cultural law

73. European nations are most likely to use which type of law?
    a. common
    b. Islamic
    c. civil (moderate, page 22)
    d. custom

74. About 70 countries, predominantly in Europe, are ruled by _____ law, as is Japan.
    a. common
    b. Islamic
    c. civil (moderate, page 22)
    d. custom

75. A _____ is an agreement by the parties concerned to establish a set of rules to govern a business transaction.
    a. procedure
    b. policy
    c. contract (moderate, page 22)
    d. rule

76. In the context of doing business in China, what is meant by the phrase "the contract is in the relationship, not on the paper"?
    a. There are no legally binding contracts in China.
    b. Contracts are torn up after they are written.
    c. Managers should not enter into contracts in China.
    d. Managers should nurture the relationship to ensure reliability of the contract. (moderate, page 22)*

77. Tariffs and quotas are examples of what types of policies?
    a. protectionist (moderate, page 22)
    b. economic development
    c. free market
    d. political development

78. In Canada, crown corporations are _____.
    a. entrepreneurial in nature
    b. wholly owned by the public sector (moderate, page 23)*
    c. owned by the private sector but managed by the public sector
    d. owned by the public sector but managed by the private sector

79.   The appropriability of technology deals with _____.
        a. technology which has been illegally appropriated by a foreign
            government
        b. how appropriate the technology is for generating long-term profit
        c. how easily the technology can be learned and used by host nation
            employees
        **d. the ability of the firm to profit from its technology by protecting
            it from its competitors (difficult, page 24) {AASCB: Uses of
            Information Technology}**

80.   Less developed countries use their investment laws to _____.
        a. acquire needed technology
        b. increase exports
        c. train local people
        d. all of the above (moderate, page 24)

81.   Which type of country is most likely to use its investment laws to
        acquire appropriate technology?
        a. post industrial
        b. newly industrializing
        c. less developed (moderate, page 24)*
        d. highly developed

82.   The International Convention for the Protection of Industrial Property is
        often referred to as the _____.
        a. Economic Union
        b. North American Free Trade Agreement
        c. Paris Union (moderate, page 24)
        d. World Trade Organization

83.   The Paris Union deals with _____.
        a. software development
        b. electronics and other high tech sales
        c. protection of patents (moderate, page 24)
        d. international cooperation in reducing pollution

84.   Some countries rigorously enforce employee secrecy agreements in
        order to _____.
        **a. protect a firm's intellectual property (easy, page 24) {AACSB:
            Uses of Information Technology}**
        b. restrict labor mobility
        c. avoid costly litigation among firms
        d. all of the above

85.   An international manager should choose technology that is _____.
    a. capital intensive
    b. labor intensive
    c. intermediate
    d. **such that it suits the level of development in the area (easy, page 24) {AACSB: Uses of Information Technology}**

86.   In a country where labor is plentiful and cheap and capital is scarce, the appropriate choice of technology for the international manager would be _____.
    a. whatever makes his job easier
    b. capital intensive
    c. **labor intensive (easy, page 24)* {AACSB: Uses of Information Technology}**
    d. all of the above

87.   _____illustrates that the Internet is not totally open and that governments make sure their laws are obeyed in cyberspace
    a. The USA banned car sales on the Internet on Sundays.
    b. Japan banned Internet gambling.
    c. **France forced Yahoo to stop displaying Nazi trinkets for sale. (moderate, page 25) {AACSB: Ethical Reasoning}**
    d. Saudi Arabia banned R rated Internet movies.

88.   While companies around the world are embracing e-commerce, there still remain several hindrances. In Europe some of these obstacles are _____.
    a. language barriers
    b. different tax systems
    c. currency issues
    d. **all of the above (moderate, page 25) {AACSB: Uses of Information Technology}**

89.   One of the ways in which the European Commission is trying to use the internet to facilitate and improve competitiveness is by _____.
    a. requiring all public sector companies to have a website
    b. mandating acceptance of credit cards by all public sector companies
    c. **advertising all tender invitations online (moderate, page 26)* {AACSB: Uses of Information Technology}**
    d. all of the above

Short Essay Questions

90.　**What is Global Management?**
Global Management is the process of developing strategies, designing and operating systems, and working with people around the world to ensure sustained competitive advantage. (easy, page 4)

91.　**Name some global brands that sell more in markets other than the country of their origin.**
Coke (USA), Ikea (Sweden), Nestlé (Switzerland), Proctor and Gamble (USA). Students should be able to find many more. (moderate, page 6)*

92.　**What is the European Union (E.U.) and what are some characteristics of it?**
The E.U now comprises a 27-nation unified market of over 400 million people. Ten countries – Cyprus, Czech Republic, Estonia, Hungary, Latvia, Lithuania, Malta, Poland, the Slovak Republic, and Slovenia joined in 2004. Bulgaria and Romania joined in 2007. Several legislative measures have been adopted to create an internal market with free movement of goods and people among the E.U. countries. 12 of these nations share a common currency, the Euro. While internal tariffs and customs duties have been largely eliminated and financial and commercial barriers have been greatly reduced, there still exists a lot of diversity among nations in terms of language and culture. (moderate, page 8)*
{AACSB: Multicultural and Diversity}

93.　**What are the dual tasks of the global manager with respect to doing business in Europe?**
The global manager will have to perform two major tasks- one is strategic, how to access "Fortress Europe" figuring out how to deal with firms outside of Europe and second is cultural- how to deal with diverse sets of languages, customs, national cultures and traditions within Europe. (moderate, page 9) **{AACSB: Multicultural and Diversity}**

94.　**How would you characterize the Chinese economy today?**
Having achieved its quest to join the World Trade Organization (WTO) in 2002, China's gross domestic product (GDP) growth rate (10.7% in 2006) has been the fastest growth rate in the world for several years. Its low wage workers and vast consumer market have attracted offshoring of manufacturing from companies around the world. For example, there are 49,000 American companies operating in China. The country, however, seems stuck halfway between a command economy and a market economy, with both private and public sector firms operating simultaneously. China attracts considerable foreign investment despite arbitrary legal systems and underdeveloped infrastructure. (moderate, page 9)*

95. **What is SAARC?**

SAARC stands for South Asia Association of Regional Cooperation - an association of seven developing South Asian nations. According to the Agreement that was effective January 1, 2006, the countries will lower tariffs by 25% within three to five years and eliminate them within seven years. Trade in South Asia is estimated at $14 billion, although the majority of that trade will take place between India and Pakistan, the two largest members. (moderate, page 10)

96. **Briefly describe the goal of the North American Free Trade Agreement (NAFTA).**

The goal of the NAFTA was to bring faster growth, more jobs, better working conditions, and a cleaner environment for Mexico, Canada and the U.S. as a result of increased exports and trade. (moderate, page 10)*

97. **What are some of the world-wide trends that affect the global economy and present new challenges for global managers?**

Sweeping political, economic, and social changes around the world present new challenges for global managers. Almost all nations today are beginning to develop decentralized, free-market systems, are moving away from communism with an increasing trend toward privatization in order to manage in a global economy of intense competition and complex high-tech industrialization. (moderate, page 10)*

98. **Why have foreign investors recently become wary of Russia?**

Until recently, Russia has been regarded as more politically stable. New land, legal, and labor codes, as well as the now-convertible ruble, have encouraged foreign firms to take advantage of opportunities in Russia, especially given the vast natural resources and well-educated population. Things have changed however. As the *Financial Times* article (May 16, 2006) quoted in the chapter states – "The investment climate is clouded by the increasing willingness…of the Russian government to intervene in the economy." This intervention was aptly illustrated by the breakup of the Yukos oil group. In addition, about two dozen companies have come under the control of the Kremlin in the last few years, including newspapers and banks. (moderate, pages 10-11)*

99. **Describe the role of information technology in fostering globalism.**
Globalism is defined as global competition characterized by networks of international linkages that bind countries, institutions, and people. Information technology, more that anything else is making those networks of international linkages more possible by boosting the efficiency of that "connectedness." The Internet is propelling electronic commerce around the world. Companies around the world are linked electronically with employees, customers, distributors, suppliers, and alliance partners in many countries making the world a global marketplace. (moderate, pages 4, 23-24)* {AACSB: Uses of Information Technology}

100. **What elements in the business environment influence the international manager's role?**
Within the larger context of global trends and competition the international manager will be influenced by a country's political and economic agenda, its technological status and level of economic development, its regulatory environment, its competitive and comparative advantages, and its cultural norms. The astute manager should assess this new environment, anticipate how it may affect the future of the home company, and then develop appropriate strategies and operating styles. (moderate, page 15)

101. **How does the phenomenon of ethnicity affect the international manager?**
Ethnicity is a driving force of political instability around the world. Many uprisings and conflicts are expressions of differences in ethnic groupings and religious disputes often lie at the heart of those differences. Managers must understand the ethnic and religious composition of the host country in order to anticipate problems of general instability as well as those of an operational nature- such as effects on their workforce, on production and access to raw materials and also the market as a whole. (moderate, pages 15-16)* {AACSB: Multicultural and Diversity}

102. **What is political risk? Give an example of how political risk can affect a MNC.**
Political risks are any government action or politically motivated event that could adversely affect the long run profitability or value of the firm. For example, Bolivia nationalized its natural gas industry ordering foreign companies to give up control of fields and accept much tougher operating terms within six months or leave the country. (moderate, pages 16-17)*

103. **What is the primary difference between expropriation and confiscation?**
Under expropriation, companies receive inadequate compensation for their assets that were seized by the local government. In contrast, confiscation refers to the seizure of assets where no compensation is provided. (moderate, page 17)

104. **Under what condition is the risk of expropriation highest?**
Expropriation is highest in countries that experience continuous political upheaval. (easy, page 17)

105. **What is the primary difference between macro and micro political risks?**
Macropolitical risk events affect all foreign firms doing business in a country or region, while micropolitical risk events affects one industry or company, or only a few companies. (easy, page 17)

106. **Identify seven of the most typical political risk events common today.**
Expropriation of corporate assets; forced sale of equity to host country nationals; discriminatory treatment in the application of laws; barriers to repatriation of funds; loss of technology or intellectual property; interference in managerial decision making; dishonesty by government officials. (difficult, page 17) {**AACSB: Ethical Reasoning**}

107. **What are the two forms of risk assessment usually taken by multinational corporations?**
One form of risk assessment is through the use of experts or consultants familiar with the country or region under consideration. A second and increasingly common means of political risk assessment used by MNCs is through the development of their own internal staff and in-house capabilities. (moderate, page 17)

108. **What is PRISM?**
Primary Risk Investment Screening Matrix. PRISM is a computer-aided model that reduces over 200 variables to an index of political and economic stability. It is a quantitative method of assessing risk. (moderate, page 18)

109. **What is "early warning system"?**
The early warning system is a method that uses lead indicators to predict political changes and potential political dangers such as signs of violence, riots, pressure to hire more local workers, or pending export-import restrictions. (moderate, page 18)

110. **Describe the two major decisions that managers face when deciding how to manage the political risk of investing or maintaining current operations in a country.**
The two major decisions are **avoidance** or **adaptation**. Managers can decide to suspend their firm's dealings with a certain country at a given point—either by the avoidance of investment or by the withdrawal of current investment. Or, they decide that the risk is relatively low in a particular country or that a high-risk environment is worth the potential returns, they may choose to start or maintain operations there and to accommodate that risk through adaptation to the political regulatory environment. (moderate, pages 18-19)*

111. **Identify and describe four means of political risk adaptation.**
The four means of political risk adaptation are: **equity sharing** – shared ownership or partial ownership with nationals; **participative management** – actively involve nationals in the management of the firm; **localization of operations** – modifications to the company's management style, company name, etc. to accommodate national issues; and **development assistance** – corporate aid for infrastructure development. (difficult, page 19)

112. **Identify and describe four means of maintaining dependency between corporations and host nations.**
The four means are: **input control** – firm maintains control over key inputs, **market control** – firm maintains control over key markets, **position control** – firm controls key management positions in the subsidiary operation, and **staged contribution strategies** – firm announces plans to increase in successive years its contributions to the host government. (difficult, page 19)

113. **What are the two common means of hedging?**
Political risk insurance local debt financing are the two means of hedging. In the U.S., political risk insurance is provided by the **Overseas Private Investment Corporation (OPIC)**. Insurance coverage is provided for the inability to repatriate profits, expropriation, nationalization, confiscation, and for damage as a result of war, and terrorism. The Foreign Credit Insurance Association (FICA) covers political risks caused by war, revolution, currency incontrovertibility, and the cancellation of import or export licenses. Political risk insurance covers the loss of a firm's assets, not the loss of revenue resulting from expropriation. The second means of hedging is **local debt financing** which refers to money borrowed in the local country. The firm would hedge its risk by withholding debt payment in lieu of sufficient compensation for its business losses.(moderate, page 19)

114. **How do companies manage terrorism risk?**
Some companies such as IBM and Exxon try to develop a benevolent image in high-risk countries through charitable contributions to the local community, maintain low profiles and minimize publicity in host countries by using discreet corporate signs at company sites. Companies also step up their security measures, hire consultants in counter-terrorism, and train employees to cope with the threat of terrorism. (moderate, pages 19-20)*

115. **What are the two most common forms of economic risk to a company?**
The two forms of economic risk to a subsidiary are 1) the risk that the government will abruptly change its domestic monetary or fiscal policies, or 2) the risk that the government will modify its foreign investment policies. The second risk would threaten the company's ability to repatriate its earnings and would create a financial or interest-rate risk. (moderate, page 20)

116. **Define currency translation exposure and give an example.**
Currency translation exposure occurs when the value of one country's currency changes relative to another. For example, a U.S. company operating in Mexico at the time of the peso devaluation in the late 1990s meant that the company's assets in that country were worth less when translated into U.S. dollars. The company's liabilities were, however, also less. (easy, page 20)

117. **According to Mathis, what are the four methods of analyzing economic risk (a country's credit worthiness)?**
The four methods are: **quantitative** (the country's ability to honor its debt obligation; **qualitative** (analyzing the types of policies the country's leaders are likely to implement); **a combination** of both qualitative and quantitative; and the **checklist** approach (use of a few easily measurable and timely criteria). (moderate, pages 20-21)

118. **What are the three international law systems and their primary distinctions?**
Common law uses past court decisions as precedents; civil law is based on a comprehensive set of laws organized into a code; Islamic law (Muslim) is based upon religious beliefs and combines in varying degrees, civil, common, and indigenous law. (moderate, page 22)

119. **Describe the differences between common law and civil law.**
In common law, past court decisions act as precedents to the interpretation of law. Civil law is based on a comprehensive set of laws organized into a code. Interpretations of civil law are based on reference to codes and statutes. (moderate, page 22)

120. **How does the government regulate business in Canada?**
The Canadian government partly or wholly owns many corporations in the transportation, petrochemicals, steel, and building materials industries. In Quebec the law requires bilingualism forcing managers to speak both French and English and to incur costs of language training for employees, translators, and the administration of paper work. (moderate, page 23)*

121. **What is the difference between appropriability of technology and appropriateness of technology?**
Appropriability refers to how readily a firm can protect its technology from being stolen or abused, while **appropriateness** refers to how adaptable that technology is to local needs. (moderate, page 24)

122. **In what ways does international law protect intellectual property rights?**
Over 80 countries adhere to the International Convention for the Protection of Industrial Property, often referred to as the Paris Union. However, differences in rule in some non-Paris union countries as well as industrial espionage activities mean that intellectual property rights are not fully guaranteed. (moderate, page 24)* {**AACSB: Uses of Information Technology**}

Comprehensive Essay Questions

123. **What are some of the economic changes that have taken place in Mexico from 1993 to 2005? Do you think NAFTA has helped the Mexican economy?**
Some economic changes are as follows. GDP increased from $403 billion in 1993 to $717 billion in 2005, with exports rising to $213 billion. In 2005, the 3% GDP growth also included remittances from migrants in the United States.

Has NAFTA helped the Mexican economy? First, it is not clear that all economic changes that have occurred in this period are attributable to NAFTA although many are. For example, Mexican trade policy is among the most open in the world and Mexico has signed 12 trade agreements with 43 countries putting 93% of its trade under free trade regulations. Most recently (in 2005), a trade agreement was signed with Japan. It is questionable whether some of the NAFTA goals have been achieved for Mexico. One goal in particular (more jobs) appears not to have been achieved, especially given the massive migration to the USA for jobs.

The situation in Mexico shows the complexity of the global business environment. For example, China now offers alternatives to Mexico for cheap offshore manufacturing for American firms. These actions have had a negative effect on the NAFTA goals of faster growth, more jobs, and increased exports and trade. (difficult, page 10)*

124. **Describe political risk insurance and local debt financing. Given the choice between political risk insurance and local debt financing, which would be most appropriate to use?**

Political risk insurance is offered by most industrialized countries. In the United States, the **Overseas Private Investment Corporation** (OPIC) provides coverage for new investments in projects in friendly, less developed countries. Insurance minimizes losses arising from specific risks – such as the inability to repatriate profits, expropriation, nationalization, or confiscation – and from damage as a result of war, terrorism. The **Foreign Credit Insurance Association** (FCIA) also covers political risks caused by war, revolution, currency inconvertibility, and the cancellation of import or export licenses. Local debt financing (money borrowed in the host country), where available, helps a firm hedge against being forced out of operation without adequate compensation. In such instances, the firm withholds debt repayment in lieu of sufficient compensation for its business losses.

Both methods have their strengths and weaknesses. It is difficult to assess them perfectly without knowing the exact cost of the insurance. Political risk insurance only covers the loss of a firm's assets, not the loss of revenue resulting from expropriation. If a firm had sufficient debt financing, it could cover cash flows for a short period of time. Also, in the threat of expropriation, the host government faces fewer local repercussions from insurance than from local debt financing. Therefore, insurance seems less of a deterrent to expropriation. (difficult, pages 19)*

125. **Discuss how a U.S. MNC's operations are affected by currency devaluation in the host country (e.g., Mexico) in which it operates. How does devaluation (e.g., the devaluation of the Russian ruble) affect Russian firms?**

Devaluation of a currency occurs when the value of that currency goes down relative to other currencies. For a U.S company operating in Mexico, the peso devaluation meant that the company's assets were worth less when translated into dollars and the financial statements: but the firm's liabilities in Mexico were also less. When the profits of the firm in Mexico firm are to be repatriated to US, the dollar amount will be smaller as a result of the devaluation. When the Russian ruble lost value in 1998, Russian firms did not have enough money to buy goods and services from overseas which meant that sales of foreign companies to Russian companies declined but foreign companies could buy more from Russian firms. Governments often devalue their currencies to encourage exports and discourage imports. However exchange rate volatility negatively affects the operations of MNCs. (moderate, pages 20)*

126. **List and discuss the four methods of analyzing economic risk, or a country's creditworthiness as recommended by John Mathis, a former senior financial policy analyst for the World Bank.**

The four methods for analyzing economic risk include: (1) the quantitative approach, (2) the qualitative approach, (3) a combination of both qualitative and quantitative approaches, and (4) the checklist approach.

The **quantitative** approach "attempts to measure statistically a country's ability to honor its debt obligation." This measure is arrived at by assigning different weights to economic variables to produce a composite index used to monitory the country's creditworthiness over time and to make comparisons with other countries. The **qualitative** approach evaluates a country's economic risk by assessing the competence of its leaders and analyzing the types of polices they are likely to implement. This approach entails a subjective assessment by the researcher in the process of interviewing those leaders and projecting the future direction of the economy. The **checklist approach** "relies on a few easily measurable and timely criteria believed to reflect or indicate changes in the creditworthiness of the country." Researchers develop various vulnerability indicators that categorize countries in terms of their ability to withstand economic volatility. (difficult, pages 20-21)

127. **What are the three major bases of law used in different regions of the world? What are the implications of these for running a company overseas?**

Common law is used in the United States and 26 other countries of British origin or influence. Under common law, past court decisions or precedents are used to interpret current situations. Civil law, used in about 27 countries (mostly in Europe), is based on a comprehensive set of laws organized into a code. Islamic law is based on religious beliefs and combines aspects of common, civil, and indigenous law. Islamic law is followed in approximately 27 countries (such as Saudi Arabia). International managers must be keenly aware of the legal infrastructure of the cultures they operate in and do everything possible to anticipate legal problems and difficulties before they occur. The legal structure of a nation has a profound impact upon behavioral patterns within the nation. (moderate, page 22)

128. **What are common types of protectionist policies used by foreign governments? How do these affect global trade? What is Japan's stance toward such policies?**

The most common types of protectionist policies are tariffs, quotas, and other types of trade restrictions imposed by countries to give their products and industries a competitive advantage. These protectionist policies raise the prices and/or restrict the quantities of imported goods thus making them more expensive to consumers and less competitive with local products. Japan has been criticized for engaging in protectionist activities by limiting imports of foreign goods while continuing to export consumer goods on a massive scale. (moderate, page 22)*

Chapter 2
Managing Interdependence
Social Responsibility and Ethics

Multiple Choice Questions

1. The most significant lesson from the Enron case was_____.
   a. the criminal behavior of the Enron executives
   b. a corporate culture poisoned by hubris and recklessness (moderate, pages 31-33)* {AACSB: Ethical Reasoning}
   c. a CEO who was unaware of criminal behavior in the organization
   d. the collapse of Enron was a result of panic in the market

2. Managers today are usually quite sensitive to issues of social responsibility and ethical behavior because of _____.
   a. interest groups
   b. legal and governmental concerns
   c. media coverage
   d. all of the above (easy, page 33)* {AACSB: Ethical Reasoning}

3. The criticisms of MNCs have been lessened in recent years because of _____.
   a. decreasing economic differences among countries
   b. emergence of multinationals from less developed countries (LDCs)
   c. greater emphasis on social responsibility by multinationals
   d. all of the above (easy, page 34)* {AACSB: Ethical Reasoning}

4. Issues of social responsibility continue to center on all of the following except _____.
   a. military industrial complex (moderate, page 34) {AACSB: Ethical Reasoning}
   b. the environment
   c. consumer concerns
   d. employees' safety and welfare

5. Some argue that MNCs already have a positive impact on LDCs by _____.
   a. providing managerial training
   b. providing investment capital
   c. creating jobs
   d. all of the above (moderate, page 34) {AACSB: Ethical Reasoning}

6. The increased complexity regarding social responsibility and ethical behavior of firms across borders is a result of _____.
   a. the distance between the home office and the subsidiaries
   b. the difficulty of training managers across cultures
   c. **the additional stakeholders associated with the firms activities (moderate, page 34) {AACSB: Ethical Reasoning}**
   d. none of the above

7. Many argue that, since MNCs operate in a global context, they should use their capital, skills, and power to play a _____ role in handling worldwide social and economic problems.
   a. cultural
   b. socioeconomic
   c. **proactive (moderate, page 34) {AACSB: Ethical Reasoning}**
   d. reactive

8. The dilemma Del Monte managers in Kenya face is _____.
   a. whether to pay the prevailing low wage to farmers or to pay higher wages
   b. whether to provide company transport to workers or let them use their own means
   c. **whether to use rich coastal lands for growing pineapples or leave the land for subsistence farming (moderate, page 34)* {AACSB: Ethical Reasoning}**
   d. all of the above

9. The sales, debts, and resources of the largest multinationals exceed the _____ of some nations.
   a. gross national product
   b. public and private debt
   c. resources
   d. **all of the above (moderate, page 34)**

10. The concept of international social responsibility is the expectation that MNCs concern themselves about _____ effects of their decisions regarding activities in other countries.
    a. philosophical
    b. competitive
    c. cultural
    d. **social and economic (moderate, page 34)* {AACSB: Ethical Reasoning}**

11. In between the corporate extremes of working solely for the interests of stockholders and working to solve social problems is the position of being _____.
   a. **socially reactive (moderate, page 32) {AACSB: Ethical Reasoning}**
   b. environmentally sensitive
   c. professionally committed
   d. ecologically proactive

12. Consensus on what should constitute moral and ethical behavior is emerging because of _____.
   a. **a global corporate culture (easy, page 35) {AACSB: Ethical Reasoning}**
   b. acceptance of American ethical values
   c. an increase in regional variation
   d. countries are becoming more ethical

13. Global corporate culture results from _____.
   a. gradual dissolution of traditional boundaries and many intricate connections among MNCs
   b. internationally linked securities markets
   c. communication networks
   d. **all of the above (moderate, page 35) {AACSB: Ethical Reasoning}**

14. Corporate social responsibility (CSR) weighted more towards "doing business right" (e.g., USA) versus CSR weighted more towards serving broader social aims (e.g., Europe) illustrates _____.
   a. **regional variations in CSR (easy, page 35) {AACSB: Ethical Reasoning}**
   b. ethnocentrism
   c. moral universalism
   d. global corporate culture

15. Moral universalism is the need for a moral standard that is accepted by _____.
   a. business corporations
   b. all governments
   c. **all cultures (moderate, page 36) {AACSB: Ethical Reasoning}**
   d. individual business professionals

16. Under ethnocentrism, a company would apply the morality used in _____.
   a. the host nation
   b. the majority of other companies in the same industry
   c. the professional codes of accountants, lawyers, and other professional groups
   d. **its own home country (easy, page 36) {AACSB: Ethical Reasoning}**

17. If McDonald's applies the morality it practices in its home country to all countries where it operates, it is an example of _____.
    a. moral universalism
    b. moral relativism
    c. ethnocentrism (moderate, page 36)* {AACSB: Ethical Reasoning}
    d. all of the above

18. A company subscribing to ethical relativism would take the approach to morality appropriate in _____.
    a. the host nation (moderate, page 36)* {AACSB: Ethical Reasoning}
    b. the majority of other companies in the same industry
    c. the professional codes of accountants, lawyers, and other professional groups
    d. its own home country

19. The future of world business with China is clouded because of _____ violations.
    a. environmental
    b. economic protectionist barriers
    c. human rights (moderate, page 36) {AACSB: Ethical Reasoning}
    d. political

20. Often the discussion of human rights centers around _____ because many of the products in the west are imported from there by western companies using manufacturing facilities located there.
    a. Asia (easy, page 37)* {AACSB: Ethical Reasoning}
    b. South America
    c. Mexico
    d. Germany

21. The Anti-Sweatshop Code of Conduct _____.
    a. includes ban on forced labor
    b. requires companies to provide a healthy and safe work environment
    c. requires companies to pay at least the prevailing local minimum wage
    d. all of the above (easy, page 37)* {AACSB: Ethical Reasoning}

22. What is SA 8000?
    a. a group of 8000 garment manufacturers in South Asia who support payment of minimum wages
    b. a Social Accountability Index fashioned around the manufacturing quality standard ISO 9000 (moderate, page 37) {AACSB: Ethical Reasoning}
    c. a classification of code for garment exporters
    d. none of the above

23. All of the following are SA 8000 proposed global labor standards that would be monitored by outside organizations except _____.
    a. provide a safe working environment
    b. **do not regularly require more than 30-hour work weeks (moderate, pages 37, 39) {AACSB: Ethical Reasoning}**
    c. respect workers' rights to unionize
    d. pay wages sufficient to meet workers' basic needs

24. The four international codes of conduct that provide some consistent guidelines for multinational enterprises were developed by all of the following except _____.
    a. **the European Union   (difficult, page 37- 39) {AACSB: Ethical Reasoning}**
    b. the International Chamber of Commerce
    c. the Organization for Economic Cooperation and Development
    d. the International Labor Organization

25. International Codes of Conduct for MNEs have three areas relating the MNE to the host government: _____, _____, and _____.
    a. **economic and development policies; laws and regulations; political involvement (moderate, page 39-40)* {AACSB: Ethical Reasoning}**
    b. political involvement; technology transfer; media relations
    c. political involvement; communication practices; media relations
    d. laws and regulations; technology transfer; communication practices

26. International business ethics refers to the business conduct or morals of MNCs in their relationship with _____.
    a. business partners
    b. political partners
    c. social systems
    d. **individuals and entities   (moderate, page 41)* {AACSB: Ethical Reasoning}**

27. According to many U.S. executives, there is little difference in ethical practices among which of the following?
    a. United States, Canada, Mexico
    b. United States, Australia, New Zealand
    c. **United States, Canada, Northern Europe   (moderate, page 42)* {AACSB: Ethical Reasoning}**
    d. Germany, France, United Kingdom

28. Which of the following is <u>false</u>?
    a. Americans treat everyone the same by making moral judgments based on general rules.
    b. Managers in Japan and Europe tend to make ethical decisions based on shared values and social ties.
    c. There is little difference in ethical practices among the USA, Canada, and N. Europe.
    d. The Japanese have the highest ethical standards (moderate, page 42) {AACSB: Ethical Reasoning}

29. What is Transparency International?
    a. A large glass manufacturing multinational corporation based in Germany
    b. A German non-governmental organization that fights corruption (moderate, page 42)
    c. An American governmental organization
    d. none of the above

30. According to Transparency International's 2005 Global Corruption Barometer for the "Business/private sector," the most corrupt region is _____ and the least corrupt region is _____.
    a. Africa, Asia
    b. Asia, Western Europe
    c. Africa, Western Europe
    d. Central and Eastern Europe, Africa (moderate, page 42)

31. The biggest single problem for MNCs, in their attempt to define a corporate-wide ethical posture, is _____.
    a. the conflicting nature of international laws
    b. the great variation of standards of ethical behavior around the world (moderate, page 45)* {AACSB: Ethical Reasoning}
    c. the absence of international legal agencies
    d. differences in worldwide religions

32. Which of the following statements is <u>false</u>?
    a. Bribery of public officials is prohibited by law in all countries.
    b. Bribery is common in parts of Africa and south and east Asia.
    c. Payments are "questionable" because of differences in laws, customs, and ethics across countries.
    d. Bribery of public officials is legal in many countries (moderate, page 45)*

33. Payments to expedite routine transactions are often referred to as _____.
   a. slotting fees
   b. grease money (moderate, page 45)*
   c. gray funds
   d. expropriation

34. In some parts of Latin America, customs officials take bribes because_____.
   a. it is legal to do so
   b. they are poorly paid (moderate, page 45)
   c. unions require customs officials to take bribes
   d. all of the above

35. A bribe differs from a gift or other reciprocation as _____.
   a. a bribe is covert in nature (difficult, page 46)*
   b. a bribe is given after the contract is awarded
   c. a bribe is large, a gift is small
   d. all of the above

36. According to Noonan, _____.
   a. many countries legally allow bribes to be paid
   b. in some countries, the newspaper lists bribe takers and givers
   c. bribery is considered universally shameful (moderate, page 46)
   d. all of the above

37. The _____ of 1977 prohibits U.S. companies from making illegal payments or other gifts or political contributions to foreign government officials for the purposes of influencing them in business transactions.
   a. Sherman Antitrust Act
   b. Robinson-Patman Act
   c. Wagner Act
   d. Foreign Corrupt Practices Act (easy, page 46)

38. In 1997, the _____convention on bribery was signed by 36 countries in an attempt to combat corruption.
   a. World Trade Organization
   b. European Union
   c. Organization for Economic Cooperation and Development (moderate, page 46)
   d. United Nations

39. Which of the following is false?
    a. The FCPA allows "grease payments' as long as they are lawful in the host country.
    b. Possible penalties for violating the FCPA include fines and imprisonment.
    c. The FCPA prohibits bribes to both government officials and private citizens (moderate, page 46).
    d. The FCPA applies only to U.S. firms.

40. Typical policies by MNCs to confront concerns about ethical behavior include all of the following except _____.
    a. develop a worldwide code of ethics
    b. consider ethical issues in strategy development
    c. develop ethical impact statements
    d. lobby host governments for ethical reform (moderate, page 47)*

41. Which of the following is not one of the important tests of ethical corporate decisions?
    a. Can you talk about it?
    b. Does it work in the short run? (moderate, page 47)
    c. Is it legal?
    d. Does it work in the long run?

42. The first line of defense for a manager in determining the "right" decision is to _____.
    a. consult his boss in the home country
    b. discuss the issue with his local agent
    c. delegate the authority to his subordinates
    d. consult the laws of both the home and host countries (moderate, page 47)

43. Which of the following is not a recommendation for making the "right" decision?
    a. Consult the International Codes of Conduct for MNEs.
    b. Consult the company's code of ethics.
    c. Consult the laws of both the home and host country.
    d. Consult the generally accepted practices in the host country (moderate, page 47-48). {AACSB: Ethical Reasoning}

44. Which of the following is not a recommendation by Richard Rhodes (CEO of Rhodes Architectural Stone) for dealing with ethical dilemmas?
    a. Establish a moral black and white.
    b. Respect cultural differences even if it means engaging in practices that are immoral by western standards (moderate, page 49)
    c. Do no business with entities which use child labor.
    d. Do no business with entities that mistreat women.

45. In Japan, corporate social responsibility has traditionally meant that the company _____.
    a. follows what its competitors are doing
    b. follows the example of the government
    c. adapts to prevailing international practices in a given region
    d. takes care of its employees (moderate, page 50)

46. Most of the past criticism levied at MNCs has focused on their activities in _____.
    a. developed nations
    b. the United States
    c. less developed countries (moderate, page 51)
    d. pollution control

47. One real or perceived lack of responsibility of MNCs focuses on the transfer-in of _____.
    a. financing and currency
    b. home nation executives
    c. different standards of living
    d. inappropriate technology (moderate, page 51)* {AACSB: Use of Information Technology}

48. The host government's typical love-hate relationship with MNCs is based on the fact that while it wants economic growth, it does not want incursions on national sovereignty nor _____.
    a. environmental problems
    b. union problems
    c. technological dependence (moderate, page 51) {AACSB: Use of Information Technology}
    d. foreign diplomacy problems

49. All of the following are criticisms of MNCs except _____.
    a. MNCs raise capital locally, crowding out local investment
    b. MNCs usually reserve key management positions for expatriates
    c. MNCs have greater wealth than the host economy (moderate, pages 51)* {AACSB: Ethical Reasoning}
    d. MNCs concentrate their R&D at home

50. MNCs run the risk of their assets becoming hostage to host control, which can take the form of all of the following except _____.
    a. nationalism
    b. privatization (moderate, page 52) {AACSB: Ethical Reasoning}
    c. protectionism
    d. governmentalism

51. Under _____, public opinion is rallied in favor of national goals and against foreign influences.
    a. nationalism (moderate, page 52)
    b. privatization
    c. protectionism
    d. governmentalism

52. Under _____, the host country institutes a partial or complete closing of borders to withstand competitive foreign products, using tariff and nontariff barriers.
    a. nationalism
    b. privatization
    c. protectionism (moderate, page 52)
    d. governmentalism

53. Which of the following is not a typical bargaining chip of host governments in their dealings with MNCs?
    a. the operation of state-owned firms
    b. regulations regarding taxes
    c. control of raw materials and market access
    d. possession of technology desired by the MNC (moderate, pages 49-51)* {AACSB: Use of Information Technology}

54. Under governmentalism, the government uses its policy-setting role to favor national interests, rather than relying on _____.
    a. market forces (moderate, page 52)
    b. stockholder interests
    c. competitive analysis
    d. environmental standards

55. According to DeGeorge, MNCs operating in developing countries should ensure that their activities _____.
    a. do no intentional harm (moderate, page 53)*
    b. change the economic system of the host country
    c. blend with the existing culture of the host country
    d. all of the above

56. In recent years, the export of hazardous wastes from developed countries to less developed ones has _____.
   a. decreased considerably
   b. remained about the same
   c. increased considerably (easy, page 54)
   d. been banned by the World Health Organization

57. What is the main reason why companies choose to dispose of hazardous waste in less developed countries?
   a. because disposing of hazardous waste in a developed countries is prohibited by international agreements
   b. to take advantage of weaker regulations and lower costs (moderate, page 54)
   c. because developing countries have the most technologically advanced waste disposal plants
   d. all of the above

58. The two main exporters of pesticides are _____.
   a. South Korea and Japan
   b. Canada and Mexico
   c. United States and France
   d. United States and Germany (moderate, page 54)

59. The selling of DDT in foreign countries by Monsanto Chemical Corporation
   a. was socially responsible since DDT was legal in those foreign countries.
   b. showed a lack of social responsibility towards the people and environment in those countries.
   c. showed a lack of social responsibility towards U.S. citizens because many fruits and meats are imported from those countries.
   d. both b and c are correct (moderate, page 54)

60. Industrial ecology requires _____.
   a. commitment from the host government
   b. that an industrial system be viewed in concert with its surrounding system (moderate, page 54) {AACSB: Use of Information Technology}
   c. home government commitment
   d. a change in host country laws

61. MNCs must take the lead in dealing with ecological interdependence by
    _____.
    a. being willing to comply with new international environmental
       regulations
    **b. integrating environmental factors with strategic planning (difficult,
       page 54)* {AACSB: Use of Information Technology}**
    c. doing more than competitors are doing
    d. cooperating with governments in drafting new environmental protection
       legislation

62. MNC managers must deal with the increasing scarcity of natural resources
    in the next few decades by _____.
    a. looking for alternate raw materials
    b. developing new methods of recycling
    c. expanding the use of byproducts
    d. all of the above (moderate, page 57)*

63. Interdependence at the local and global level requires that the moral duty for
    the MNC is_____.
    a. Establish a single clear posture towards social and ethical
       responsibilities
    b. Ensure that social and ethical responsibilities are properly implemented
    c. Respect local laws, policies, traditions, culture, and economic needs
    d. all of the above (easy, page 54)

Short Essay Questions

64. **What is the distinction between ethics and social responsibility?**
    Ethics deals with decisions and interactions on an individual basis, while
    social responsibility deals with broader decisions that affect the entire
    corporation. (easy, page 34)

65. **What are some of the concerns regarding the social responsibility of
    MNCs, especially in the less developed countries?**
    Issues of social responsibility continue to center on poverty and lack of equal
    opportunity around the world, the environment, consumer safety concerns,
    and employee safety and welfare. Many believe that MNCs should use their
    capital, skills, and power to solve social and economic problems. Others
    argue that MNCs already have a positive effect on less developed countries by
    providing investment and jobs. (moderate, page 34)*

66. **What is the degree or level of social responsibility that a domestic form should assume?**
The degree or level of social responsibility that a firm should assume ranges from one extreme of only making a profit (within the confines of the law) to the other extreme of anticipating and solving the problems of society. (easy, page 34) {AACSB: Ethical Reasoning}

67. **Why is a firm's stance toward social responsibility in its international operations more complex than purely domestic operations?**
The increasing complexity of social responsibility and ethical behavior of firms across borders is brought about by the additional stakeholders in the firm's activities through operating overseas. (moderate, page 34)

68. **What is the relationship between global corporate culture and moral universalism?**
The emergence of a global corporate culture (i.e., the integration of the business environments in which businesses operate) is leading towards global consensus about social responsibility (i.e. moral universalism). Despite this trend, however, there are regional variations in how companies respond to corporate social responsibility. (moderate, page 35)

69. **Explain the differences between the moral universalism, the ethnocentric approach, and ethical relativism. Which approach is best?**
When using the ethnocentric approach, the company applies the morality of its home country. In contrast, a company using ethical relativism adopts the moral code of the country in which it is doing business. Moral universalism is different in that it neither applies a moral code that is based on the home or host country, but rather uses a set of universal standards or codes that are derived from international codes of conduct. Ethics researcher Bowie argues that moral universalism is preferable to ethnocentrism and relativism as a guide for ethical decision making. (moderate, page 36)

70. **Why would MNCs like to follow the Anti Sweatshop Code of Conduct?**
The Anti Sweatshop Code of Conduct was established by former President Clinton and provides a ban on forced labor, abuse, and discrimination. It requires, among other things, that companies provide a healthy and safe work environment and pay the prevailing local minimum wage. The Department of Labor publishes the names of companies that comply with this code, including Nike, Reebok, Liz Claiborne, Wal-Mart, and Phillips-Van Heusen. (moderate, page 37)* {AACSB: Ethical Reasoning}

71. **List five proposed global labor standards (SA8000) that would be monitored by outside organizations to certify that plants are meeting minimal ethical standards.**
The five proposed global labor standards include: (1) do not use child or forced labor, (2) provide a safe working environment, (3) respect workers' rights to unionize, (4) do not regularly require more than 48-hour work weeks, and (5) pay wages sufficient to meet workers' basic needs. (moderate, pages 37, 39)

72. **Identify four organizations that have developed codes of conduct for international companies.**
International Chamber of Commerce, Organization for Economic Cooperation and Development, International Labor Organization, and The United Nations Commission on Transnational Corporations. (difficult, page 39)

73. **Four international codes of conduct for MNEs were developed by a number of international organizations. Which areas of MNE behavior did the codes cover?**
MNEs and Host Governments; MNEs and the Public; MNEs and Persons; and Human Rights. (moderate, pages 39-41)

74. **Define and discuss the purpose of the Foreign Corrupt Practices Act (FCPA) of 1977.**
The Foreign Corrupt Practices Act prohibits U.S. companies from making illegal payments or other gifts, or political contributions to foreign government officials for the purpose of influencing them in business transactions. The goal was to stop MNCs from contributing to corruption in foreign governments, and to upgrade the image of the U.S. and its companies operating overseas. (moderate, page 46)*

75. **According to American managers, what impact has the Foreign Corrupt Practices Act had on their ability to do business in certain countries?**
Many managers believe that the FCPA has given them a more even playing field because they are now able to do business in countries where previously it was difficult to operate without bribery and kickbacks. (easy, page 46)*

76. **What are the worldwide practices that MNCs have developed as a means of confronting concerns of ethical behavior and social responsibility?**
Develop worldwide codes of ethics; consider ethical issues in strategy development; develop periodic "ethical impact" statements; and consider withdrawing from problem countries if ethical problems are unsolvable. (moderate, page 47)

77. **What are some of the major criticisms of MNC subsidiary activities?**
MNC borrowing activities cause interest rates to rise in host countries; host country people have little control or ownership over MNC operations within their borders; MNCs save key managerial and technical positions for expatriates; MNCs do not adapt technology to fit local conditions; MNCs emphasize demand for luxury goods in host countries rather than essential goods; MNCs buy local firms rather than starting new ones; and, MNCs are not accountable to their host nations. (difficult, pages 51)* {**AACSB: Use of Information Technology**}

78. **Explain the bases of power of both the MNC and the host government.**
MNC power is based on their large-scale, worldwide operations, strategic flexibility, access to technology, and production location. Host government power is based on control of raw material and market access, and the ability to develop laws governing private enterprise, the role of state-owned firms, and other matters involving foreign investment. (moderate, page 52)*

79. **Define and describe the concept of industrial ecology.**
An industrial system must be viewed in concert with surrounding systems so as to optimize the total materials cycle from virgin material to ultimate disposal. (moderate, page 54) {**AACSB: Use of Information Technology**}

80. **How must MNC managers deal with the increasing scarcity of natural resources?**
At the least, MNC managers must deal with the increasing scarcity of natural resources in the next few decades by: (1) looking for alternate raw materials, (2) developing new methods of recycling or disposing of used materials, and (3) expanding the use of byproducts. (moderate, page 54)* {**AACSB: Use of Information Technology**}

Comprehensive Essay Questions

81. **"When in Rome, do as the Romans do". Would this be a suitable guideline for MNC's doing business in developing countries with respect to ethical practices and social responsibility? Discuss.**

It would be quite easy for MNCs to adopt and follow the business practices of host countries with respect to ethical standards and social responsibility. However, MNC stakeholders expect that when MNCs operate in the global context, they should use their capital, skills and power to play a proactive role in handling worldwide social and economic problems and be concerned with host country welfare. It is in this context that MNC's should follow the highest ethical standards with respect to questionable payments as practical business considerations allow. Many MNCs have clear-cut policies regarding payment of bribes, kickbacks to suppliers etc. U.S MNCs are subject to the provisions of the Foreign Corrupt Practices Act 1977 that prohibits U.S companies from making illegal payments or other gifts or political contributions to foreign government officials for the purposes of influencing them in business transactions. As far as social responsibility is concerned, MNCs should concern themselves with issues of use of hazardous technology, poverty and lack of equal opportunity, environment, consumer concerns and employee safety and welfare. Several international agencies have developed codes of conduct for MNCs operating in less developed countries just so MNCs do not exploit host countries under the guise of "When in Rome, do as the Romans do." (difficult, pages 34-50)* {**AACSB: Ethical Reasoning**}

82. **How is a manager operating abroad to know what is the "right" decision when faced with questionable or unfamiliar circumstances of doing business?**

First, one should consult the laws of both the home and the host countries. If any of those laws would be violated, then you, the manager, must look to some other way to complete the business transaction, or withdraw altogether. Secondly, you could consult the international codes of conduct for MNEs. These are broad and cover various areas of social responsibility and ethical behavior. If legal consultation does not provide you with a clear answer about what to do, you should consult the company's code of ethics (if there is one). Also, as the manager, you should realize that you are not alone in making these kinds of decisions. It is also the responsibility of the company to provide guidelines for the actions and decisions made by its employees. (moderate, page 47)* {**AACSB: Ethical Reasoning**}

83. **What are some of the criticisms of MNCs operating in developing countries? What recommendations could you make to an MNC to avoid these criticisms?**

Criticisms of MNC subsidiary activities in less developed countries are along these lines: MNCs often raise their needed capital locally (to reduce risk), contributing to a rise in interest rates in host countries; the majority (sometimes even 100 percent) of the stock of most subsidiaries is owned by the parent company. Consequently, host-country people do not have much control over the operations of corporations within their borders; MNCs usually reserve the key managerial and technical positions for expatriates. As a result, they may not immediately contribute to the development of host-country personnel; MNCs may not adapt their technology to the conditions that exist in host countries; MNCs concentrate their research and development activities at home restricting the transfer of technology; MNCs are not accountable to their host nations but only respond to home-country governments; they are not concerned with host-country plans for development.

Implementing DeGeorge's recommendations for doing business in developing countries is one method of addressing the criticisms. De George recommends the following for MNCs:
   a. Do no intentional harm (including respect for the ecosystem and consumer safety)
   b. Produce more good than harm for the host country.
   c. Contribute to the host country's development.
   d. Respect the human rights of employees.
   e. To the extent that local culture does not violate ethical norms, respect the local culture and work with not against it.
   f. Pay fair share of taxes.
   g. Cooperate with the local government in developing and enforcing just background institutions (i.e., laws, governmental regulations, unions, and consumer groups). (difficult, pages 51, 53)*
      {AACSB: Ethical Reasoning}

84. **List and discuss the three forms by which MNCs run the risk of their assets becoming hostage to host control.**

The three forms include nationalism, protectionism, and governmentalism. Under nationalism, public opinion is rallied in favor of national goals and against foreign influences. Under protectionism, the host institutes a partial or complete closing of borders to withstand competitive foreign products, using tariff and nontariff barriers. Under governmentalism, the government uses its policy-setting role to favor national interests, rather than relying on market forces. (moderate, page 52)* {AACSB: Ethical Reasoning}

Chapter 3
Understanding the Role of Culture

Multiple Choice Questions

1.   An importer halted sales of the Japanese game Pokémon in Saudi Arabia because _____.
     a.   **the game might encourage the un-Islamic practice of gambling (moderate, page 87)***
     b.   children in Saudi Arabia were afraid of Pokemon
     c.   Saudi Arabia charged very heavy duty on imports from Japan
     d.   all of the above

2.   In Saudi Arabia, women account for _____ percent of the workforce.
     a.   51
     b.   45
     c.   15
     d.   **7 (moderate, page 88)***

3.   Which of the following is <u>false</u> about the restrictions placed on women in Saudi Arabia?
     a.   **They are not allowed to be teachers or doctors (moderate, page 88)**
     b.   They are not allowed to be engineers.
     c.   The are not allowed to drive.
     d.   They are not allowed to be flight attendants on Saudi Arabian Airlines.

4.   Which of the following is an example of adjustments that firms have made to accommodate the restrictions on women in Saudi Arabia?
     a.   Pizza Hut installed two dining rooms – one for single men, and one for families.
     b.   Saks Fifth Avenue created women-only floors.
     c.   Companies have installed separate work entrances for women.
     d.   **All of the above are examples of adjustments (easy, page 88)**

5.   Why do high-end department stores and famous designers operate in Saudi Arabia given the dress restrictions for both men and women?
     a.   There are parts of Saudi Arabia where dress restrictions do not apply.
     b.   Women wear designer clothes only in front of their husbands or other women.
     c.   Wealthy men wear the latest high-end fashions when traveling abroad.
     d.   **Both b and c are correct (moderate, page 89)***

6.   _____ is having a working knowledge of the cultural variables affecting management decisions.
a. Cultural sensitivity
b. Cultural accommodation
c. Cultural transfer
d. **Cultural savvy (easy, page 90) {AACSB: Multicultural and Diversity}**

7.   _____ is an awareness and an honest caring about another individual's culture.
a. Cultural accommodation
b. **Cultural empathy (moderate, page 90) {AACSB: Multicultural and Diversity}**
c. Cultural sympathy
d. Cultural transfer

8.   According to research by Black and Mendenhall, up to _____ of expatriate managers leave their assignments early because of poor performance or poor adjustment in the local environment.
a. 10%
b. **40% (difficult, page 91)**
c. 20%
d. 25%

9.   AT&T executives were the first to admit that one of the greatest challenges of putting an international venture together was _____.
a. the financial risks involved
b. **partners frequently see the world in different ways (difficult, page 91)***
c. employees do not want to work hard in certain cultures
d. managers are ethnocentric

10.   The culture of a society comprises_____.
a. shared values
b. understandings
c. goals
d. **all of the above (easy, page 91) {AACSB: Multicultural and Diversity}**

11. Which of the following research findings is <u>false</u>?
    a. Cross-cultural differences are the main cause of failed negotiations and interactions.
    b. U.S. firms lose over $2 billion per year to failed expatriate assignments.
    c. Cross-cultural training is ineffective in developing skills and enhancing adjustment and performance (moderate, page 91) {AACSB: Multicultural and Diversity}
    d. U.S. firms do little to incorporate cross-cultural training into their ongoing training programs.

12. Cultural variables (values, norms, and beliefs) determine basic attitudes towards _____.
    a. work, and time
    b. materialism, and individualism
    c. change
    d. all of the above (moderate, page 92) {AACSB: Multicultural and Diversity}

13. The culture of _____ in the Netherlands was incorporated into business policy when KLM Royal Dutch Airlines revised its travel-benefits policy for families of employees.
    a. financial performance
    b. cost control
    c. human relations development
    d. social responsiveness (moderate, page 92)*

14. The changes made by KLM in the Netherlands illustrated _____.
    a. bilingual versus monolingual employees
    b. male versus female employees
    c. pay differences between men and women
    d. organizational culture responding to national cultural values (moderate, page 92)*

15. Convergence occurs when _____.
    a. management styles evolve into entirely different styles over time
    b. management styles become more similar to one another (difficult, page 93) {AACSB: Multicultural and Diversity}
    c. managers agree to disagree on how to manage
    d. employees and managers begin to behave alike

16. A self-reference criterion means that we _____.
    a. refer to the opinions of others in forming our own opinions
    b. **unconsciously refer to our own cultural values (difficult, page 93) {AACSB: Multicultural and Diversity}**
    c. refer to other cultures in trying to understand our own better
    d. understand our culture more than we understand other cultures

17. Several Japanese workers at a U.S. manufacturing plant had to learn how to _____ when there was trouble.
    a. **put courtesy aside and interrupt conversations (difficult, page 93)* {AACSB: Communication}**
    b. speak more rapidly
    c. treat men differently from women
    d. interpret American slang

18. Europeans can be fooled by a deceiving appearance of _____ in American business.
    a. objectivity
    b. **informality (moderate, page 93)***
    c. formality
    d. professionalism

19. The first step toward cultural sensitivity is for an international manager to _____.
    a. work in another culture
    b. interact with people from different cultures
    c. **understand his or her own culture (moderate, page 94)**
    d. learn to speak another language

20. _____ occurs when a Frenchman, for example, expects those from or in another country to automatically fall into patterns of behavior common in France.
    a. Geocentricism
    b. Regiocentricism
    c. **Parochialism (moderate, page 94)* {AACSB: Multicultural and Diversity}**
    d. Ethnocentrism

21. Which of the following describes the attitude of those who operate from the assumption that their ways of doing things are best—no matter where or under what conditions they are applied?
    a. geocentricism
    b. regiocentricism
    c. parochialism
    d. **ethnocentrism (moderate, page 94)* {AACSB: Multicultural and Diversity}**

22. Procter & Gamble made a business mistake in Japan in the area of
    _____.
    a. distribution
    b. product quality
    c. product design
    d. advertising (easy, page 94)*

23. How can a student of cross-cultural management develop an understanding of a particular culture?
    a. Develop a cultural profile for that country or region in which the firm does business (easy, page 95) {AACSB: Multicultural and Diversity}
    b. Assume that American cultural styles and practices can be successfully transplanted.
    c. Use stereotypes as a basic guide to develop your cultural understanding.
    d. Both a and c are correct.

24. Which of the following is a reason for <u>not</u> stereotyping people according to their national cultural norms?
    a. Current measures of culture are grossly inaccurate.
    b. Many cultures have diverse subcultures. (difficult, page 87)* {AACSB: Multicultural and Diversity}
    c. Stereotyping is always wrong.
    d. There really is no such thing as national cultural differences.

25. Which of the following is <u>not</u> a cultural variable?
    a. kinship
    b. education
    c. religion
    d. career choice (easy, page 96)

26. Research by Harris and Moran identified eight categories that form _____ in every society.
    a. subsystems (moderate, page 96)
    b. stereotypes
    c. culturally sensitive pockets
    d. cultural misunderstandings

27. The main contribution of Harris and Moran's eight categories is:
    a. To show how subsystems in a society affect that society's culture and individual behavior (moderate, pages 95-98)
    b. To show how stereotyping can be a useful method to learn about cultures.
    c. To show how subcultures are beginning to converge with broader cultures.
    d. To show the eight most common mistakes made by American managers.

28. Kinship systems relate most closely to _____.
    a. workplace relations
    b. relationships between friends
    c. **family relationships (moderate, page 96)**
    d. relationships between superiors and subordinates

29. When an American-educated Asian presented a business plan to his uncle, what problem emerged?
    a. The uncle was insulted because of his nephew's educational background.
    b. Employees felt they should have been included in the decision.
    c. **An astrologer included in the meeting vetoed the plan. (difficult, page 96)***
    d. The uncle was insulted that his nephew conducted the meeting in English rather than Japanese.

30. Which category of values is most likely to underlie both moral and economic norms?
    a. economic
    b. historical
    c. **religious (moderate, page 96-97)**
    d. personal

31. The economic system of a country has powerful influence on such organizational processes as _____.
    a. sourcing
    b. distribution
    c. repatriation of capital
    d. **all of the above (easy, page 96)**

32. Which religious group places the greatest emphasis on the concept of "God willing?"
    a. Hindus
    b. Buddhists
    c. Catholics
    d. **Muslims (moderate, page 97)***

33. The Islamic law of Sharia relates most directly to what aspect of business?
    a. selling
    b. pricing
    c. **charging interest (moderate, page 97)***
    d. employee training

34. The modern Western system of _____ is technically illegal in Muslim nations.
    a. steel
    b. consumer products
    c. textiles
    d. banking (easy, page 97)

35. _____ are a society's ideas about what is good or bad, right or wrong—such as the widespread belief that stealing is immoral and unfair.
    a. Laws
    b. Values (moderate, page 98)
    c. Rules
    d. Procedures

36. According to the GLOBE project, _____ dimension refers to how much people in a society are expected to be tough, confrontational and competitive versus modest and tender.
    a. Humane orientation
    b. Assertiveness (moderate, page 98)
    c. Future orientation
    d. Performance orientation

37. People from Singapore and Switzerland attach a high level of importance to behaviors such as planning and investing for the future. According to the GLOBE project such societies have a _____.
    a. performance orientation
    b. assertiveness orientation
    c. humane orientation
    d. future orientation (easy, page 98)*

38. People from Singapore, Hong Kong and USA tend to take initiative and have a sense of urgency and the confidence to get things done. Such people are _____ oriented according to the GLOBE project.
    a. humane
    b. future
    c. performance (easy, page 99)*
    d. all of the above

39. Which of the following was <u>not</u> included in Hofstede's scheme of international value dimensions?
    a. uncertainty avoidance
    b. involvement in relationships (moderate, page 100)
    c. power distance
    d. individualism

40. Cultures which display high power distance will probably have _____.
    a. decentralized structure
    b. **autocratic leadership (moderate, pages 100-101)**
    c. loosely defined chain of command
    d. lack of formality between workers

41. An autocratic style of management would be best received in which of the following situations?
    a. low power-distance countries
    b. **high power-distance countries (moderate, pages 100-101)**
    c. uncertainty avoiding countries
    d. countries with low individualism

42. Societies such as Malaysia, Mexico and Philippines that accept strong hierarchical boss-subordinate relationships tend to score high on Hofstede's _____ dimension.
    a. uncertainty avoidance
    b. collectivism
    c. masculinity
    d. **power distance (easy, pages 100-101)* {AACSB: Multicultural and Diversity}**

43. According to Hofstede's value dimensions, _____ is the level of acceptance by a society of the unequal distribution of power in institutions.
    a. **power distance (easy, pages 100-101) {AACSB: Multicultural and Diversity}**
    b. uncertainty avoidance
    c. individualism
    d. masculinity

44. Which of the Hofstede variables would be most closely responsible for the existence of formal rules and procedures within a given culture?
    a. individualism
    b. **uncertainty avoidance (moderate, page 101) {AACSB: Multicultural and Diversity}**
    c. masculinity
    d. femininity

45. According to Hofstede's value dimensions, _____ refers to the tendency of people to look after themselves and their immediate family only and neglect the needs of society.
    a. power distance
    b. uncertainty avoidance
    c. **individualism (moderate, page 102) {AACSB: Multicultural and Diversity}**
    d. masculinity

46. According to Hofstede, countries such as Japan, Portugal, and Greece have strict laws and procedures to which their people adhere closely because they have _____, while countries like Denmark, Great Britain, and U.S. tolerate protests because they have _____.
    a. high power distance; high uncertainty avoidance
    b. high masculinity; low individualism
    c. **high uncertainty avoidance; low uncertainty avoidance (moderate, page 101)* {AACSB: Multicultural and Diversity}**
    d. high individualism; low individualism

47. Jane greatly values achievements and success. Fred on the other hand, values time with family and friends. Based on Hofstede's cultural dimensions, Jane is likely to come from a _____ culture, while Fred is likely to come from a _____ culture.
    a. high power distance; low power distance
    b. high risk loving; low risk loving
    c. **individualistic; collectivist (difficult, page 102)* {AACSB: Multicultural and Diversity}**
    d. achievement oriented; performance oriented

48. According to Hofstede's research, there is a strong relationship among _____, wealth, and a political system balanced with power.
    a. low individualism
    b. **high individualism (moderate, page 102) {AACSB: Multicultural and Diversity}**
    c. low uncertainty avoidance
    d. high power-distance

49. Which of the following is <u>not</u> a masculine value?
    a. **Concern for the quality of life (easy, page 102) {AACSB: Multicultural and Diversity}**
    b. lack of concern for others
    c. assertiveness
    d. materialism

50. Which of the following describes the position of U.S. culture with respect to masculinity?
    a. **medium (moderate, page 102) {AACSB: Multicultural and Diversity}**
    b. low
    c. high
    d. non-existent

51. In a comparative study of the U.S. and China, Earley found that the Chinese performed _____ when working as a group than working alone and the American performed _____ due to "social loafing."
    a. better; worse (difficult, page 102)*
    b. worse; better
    c. both societies performed equally
    d. the study was inconclusive
    e.

52. Which of the following is <u>not</u> a value dimension in Trompenaars's system?
    a. universalism vs. particularism
    b. neutral vs. affective
    c. specific vs. diffuse
    d. doing vs. being (moderate, page 104-105)

53. Concerning Trompenaars's value dimensions, which of the following is related to the universalistic obligation?
    a. the application of rules and systems objectively (moderate, page 104)
    b. open expression of emotions
    c. most weight placed on relationships
    d. separation of work and private life

54. Concerning Trompenaars's value dimensions, which of the following is related to the particularistic obligation?
    a. the application of rules and systems objectively
    b. open expression of emotions
    c. most weight placed on relationships (moderate, page 104)
    d. separation of work and private life

55. Concerning Trompenaars's value dimensions, which of the following is a characteristic of the diffuse culture?
    a. puts emphasis on relationships and is more subjective
    b. applies rules and systems objectively
    c. separates work and private life
    d. work spills over into private life and vice versa (moderate, page 104)

56. Jane passes on insider information to Jill, her friend. According to Trompenaars, Jane likely comes from _____ society.
    a. a particularistic (difficult, pages 104)
    b. an universalistic
    c. an achievement
    d. an ascription

57. According to Trompenaars, the _____ dimension focuses on the emotional orientation of relationships.
    a. universalism versus particularism
    b. neutral versus affective (moderate, page 104)
    c. specific versus diffuse
    d. achievement versus ascription

58. Italians and Mexicans would openly express emotions even in a business situation, where as British and Japanese would consider such displays unprofessional. Trompenaars categorizes the differences as _____.
    a. universalism versus particularism
    b. neutral versus affective (moderate, page 104)*
    c. specific versus diffuse
    d. achievement versus ascription

59. As far as involvement in relationships goes, managers in _____ cultures separate work and personal issues and relationships; they compartmentalize their work and private lives, and they are more open and direct.
    a. diffuse-oriented
    b. specific-oriented (moderate, page 104)
    c. universal-oriented
    d. particular-oriented

60. In which of the following value dimensions according to Trompenaars is the question "what is the source of power and status in society?"
    a. universalism versus particularism
    b. neutral versus affective
    c. specific versus diffuse
    d. achievement versus ascription (moderate, pages 104-105)

61. In an achievement society, the source of status may be based on _____.
    a. your father's occupation
    b. your mother's family status
    c. the level of education you attain (moderate, page 104)
    d. your gender

62. In an ascription-oriented society, people may ascribe status on the basis of _____.
    a. education
    b. job rank
    c. salary earned
    d. gender (easy, page 105)* {AACSB: Multicultural and Diversity}

63. Bukra in Arabic means _____.
    a. "this can never happen"
    b. "God will decide"
    c. "tomorrow or sometime in the future" (moderate, page 105)
    d. "yesterday or sometime in the past"

64. Some culturally based variables that cause frequent problems for
    Americans in international management include_____, _____,
    _____, and _____.
    a. People, countries, cultures, and stereotypes
    b. Language, culture, religion, and politics
    **c. Time, change, material factors, and individualism (easy, pages
       105-106)**
    d. Attitudes, poverty, prejudice, and materialism

65. While Americans usually regard a deadline as _____, Arabs often regard a
    deadline as _____.
    a. a guideline; a firm commitment
    b. a firm commitment; an insult (moderate, page 105)*
    c. a flexible time limit; a guideline
    d. a guideline; an issue

66. To the Chinese, the introduction of power machinery meant that the worker
    had to throw over not only habits of work but also _____.
    a. family responsibility
    b. leisure time
    c. sense of personal dignity
    d. ideology (moderate, page 106)*

67. Western societies consider change as _____, whereas many non-western
    societies consider it as_____.
    a. externally controlled; controlled by the individual
    b. negative; positive
    c. being too slow; being too fast.
    **d. controlled by the individual; externally controlled (difficult, page
       105)**

68. What is the attitude of Indians or Koreans toward nature?
    a. They fear it.
    b. They consider it a part of religious beliefs. (moderate, page 106)*
    c. It is to be overcome.
    d. It is there primarily for leisure time.

69. The example of Sweden barring U.S airlines from transmitting passenger information such as wheelchair need and meal preferences illustrates:
    a. Higher Internet use in Sweden compared to the U.S.
    b. Lax enforcement of privacy in Sweden
    c. The effect of the Internet on a country's culture
    d. The effect of culture on how the Internet is used (moderate, page 108) {AACSB: Multicultural and Diversity}

70. The manner in which Europe views information privacy has its roots in
    a. the acceptance of U.S. cultural practices
    b. the formation of the European Union
    c. culture and history (easy, page 108) {AACSB: Multicultural and Diversity}
    d. the spread of technological innovations

71. Which of the following is not a characteristic of Americans, according to the research of Harris and Moran?
    a. competitive and aggressive
    b. generous
    c. friendly and informal
    d. stable values from one generation to the next (moderate, pages 109-110)

72. According to Harris and Moran, Americans can be characterized by which of the following traits?
    a. goal oriented (moderate, pages 109-110)
    b. formal
    c. fixed traditional values
    d. reliant on others

73. Based on the research of Hofstede and England, and studies of cultural profiles of other countries, which of the following values is <u>not</u> high in Japan?
    a. individualism (moderate, page 109*) {AACSB: Multicultural and Diversity}
    b. masculinity
    c. uncertainty avoidance
    d. power distance

74. Much of Japanese culture-and the basis of working relationships-can be explained by the principle of
    a. wa (easy, page 111)
    b. Tao
    c. Femininity
    d. Low power distance

75. The concept of "wa" in Japanese culture means _____.
    a. productivity
    b. peace and harmony (moderate, page 111)
    c. group
    d. duty

76. The concept of "amae" in Japanese culture means _____.
    a. saving face
    b. working because of duty
    c. putting the interests of other first
    d. indulgent love (moderate, page 111)

77. Which of the following does <u>not</u> characterize the Japanese business environment?
    a. strong working relationships
    b. strong seniority systems
    c. weak middle management (moderate, page 111)*
    d. emphasis on looking after employees

78. According to Hall and Hall, the German preference for closed doors and private space are evidence of the affinity for_____in organizations and their own lives.
    a. compartmentalization (difficult, page 113)*
    b. high power distance
    c. authority
    d. obedience

79. Which of the following does <u>not</u> accurately characterize Koreans?
    a. high ranking in collectivism and pragmatism
    b. moderate power distance
    c. low uncertainty avoidance (moderate, page 113)* {AACSB: Multicultural and Diversity}
    d. low masculinity

80. Which of the following does <u>not</u> accurately characterize Koreans?
    a. aggressive
    b. supportive of participative management (moderate, page 113) {AACSB: Multicultural and Diversity}
    c. emotionally demonstrative
    d. formal

81. Korea and its people have undergone great changes, but respect for _____ remains strong.
    a. family
    b. authority
    c. formality
    d. all of the above (moderate, page 113) {AACSB: Multicultural and Diversity}

82 In Arab culture, people value _____ over the work at hand and verbal accuracy.
    a. personal relationships
    b. honor
    c. saving face
    d. all of the above (easy, page 116) {AACSB: Multicultural and Diversity}

83. Which of the following is not a characteristic of Arab culture?
    a. open admission of errors (moderate, page 116) {AACSB: Multicultural and Diversity}
    b. high context communication style
    c. polychromic use of time
    d. importance of preserving honor

84. "*Guanxi* provides the little red engine of business transactions in China." *Guanxi* refers to _____.
    a. a network of relationships (easy, page, 117)*
    b. giving bribes
    c. government approvals
    d. adequate power supply

85. Which of the following is not a characteristic of the Chinese business culture?
    a. paternalism
    b. autocratic leadership
    c. mutual obligation
    d. absence of hierarchy (easy, page 116)

Short Essay Questions

86. **What is generally understood by the term "culture"?**
The culture of a society generally comprises the shared values, understandings, assumptions, and goals that are shared by members of that society. This shared outlook results in common attitudes, codes of conduct and norms of behavior. Culture is generally learnt by the socialization process and passed on to succeeding generations. (easy, pages 91-92)*

87. **What are some of the restrictions placed on women in Saudi Arabia? To what extent are women involved in economic and other activities in Saudi Arabia?**
Even though Saudi Arabia ratified an agreement in 2000 designed to eliminate discrimination against women, the country still places restrictions on what women can and cannot do. On the one hand, women outnumber men in Saudi universities (there are separate male and female universities), and Saudi women comprise a large portion of teachers and doctors. In the workforce however, women make up only 7 percent. They own about 20% of all Saudi businesses (but can sell only to women). Women are not allowed to drive, to have private law or architectural firms, or to be engineers. They must cover their hair in public and are not allowed to work alongside men. (moderate, page 88) {AACSB: Ethical Reasoning}

88. **Explain how national culture can affect the business and management practices of a firm. Use an example from the chapter.**
The KLM Royal Dutch Airlines example in the text illustrates how the Dutch culture of social responsiveness influenced KLM's decision to change its policy on travel benefits for employee families. For some time, KLM stewards had protested the rule that allowing only immediate family members to be eligible for low fares (including just-married heterosexual couples) but excluding long-term homosexual partners. Upon reconsideration, KLM changed the policy so that any couple who registered as living together would be eligible. By changing its policy, KLM placed emphasis on committed relationships rather than marital status or sexual preference. (moderate, pages 92-93)* {AACSB: Multicultural and Diversity}

89. **Explain the difference between parochialism and ethnocentrism.**
Parochialism occurs when a Frenchman, for example, expects those from or in another country to automatically fall into patterns of behavior common in France. Ethnocentrism describes the attitude of those who operate from the assumption that their ways of doing things are best—no matter where or under what conditions they are applied. (moderate, page 94)

90. **Why might banks encounter difficulties operating in Muslim cultures?**
The Islamic concept of Sharia condemns the paying of interest, making it difficult for banks to operate in Muslim cultures. (moderate, page 97)*
{AACSB: Multicultural and Diversity}

91. **Why are GLOBE clusters helpful to multinational managers?**
The GLOBE research team analyzed data on nine cultural dimensions across 62 countries. Some later research by one of the GLOBE team members found 10 cultural clusters: South Asia, Anglo, Arab, Germanic Europe, Latin Europe, Eastern Europe, Confucian Asia, Latin America, Sub-Saharan Africa, and Nordic Europe. Knowing which countries are culturally similar (i.e., in the same cluster) is helpful to MNC managers since it is less risky and more profitable to expand into similar cultures rather than those that are drastically different. Besides, having learnt a successful management style in one country, managers can readily use it in another country that belongs to the same cluster. (difficult, page 100)*

92. **List the nine GLOBE cultural dimensions which distinguish one society from another and have important managerial implications.**
The nine cultural dimensions are assertiveness, future orientation, performance orientation, humane orientation, gender differentiation, uncertainty avoidance, power distance, institutional collectivism versus individualism, and in-group collectivism. (moderate, page 98)

93. **What are the five value dimensions in Hofstede's research?**
The five value dimensions are: power distance, uncertainty avoidance, individualism, masculinity, and long-term/short-term orientation. (Alternatively, you may ask for definitions of the five value dimensions in Hofstede's research and use the terms section as an answer key). (moderate, pages 100-103) **{AACSB: Multicultural and Diversity}**

94. **Why should one be cautious when interpreting the findings of Hofstede?**
Hofstede's findings were based on research from only one sample company IBM. Hofstede also does not account for within country differences in multicultural countries (such as Belgium or Switzerland). If used with the knowledge of these limitations, however, Hofstede's research is a valuable guide to understanding basic cultural differences among countries. (moderate, page 100)* **{AACSB: Multicultural and Diversity}**

95. **According to Hofstede, what is the relationship between individualism and national economic performance?**
His research has shown that strongly individualistic cultures tend to have both a higher gross national product and a freer political system than those countries scoring low on individualism. There is a strong relationship among individualism, wealth, and a political system with balanced power. (moderate, page 102)* {AACSB: **Multicultural and Diversity**}

96. **List the four value dimensions according to Trompenaars.**
The four value dimensions are (1) universalism versus particularism, (2) neutral versus affective, (3) specific or diffuse, and (4) achievement versus ascription. (easy, pages 103-105) {AACSB: **Multicultural and Diversity**}

97. **What are the characteristics of a universalist culture (such as the United States) vs. a particularist culture (such as China)?**
A universalist culture applies rules and systems objectively, without consideration for individual circumstances. In contrast, a particularist culture gives more weight to relationships and is more subjective. (moderate, pages 104)* {AACSB: **Multicultural and Diversity**}

98. **What are the characteristics of managers in specific cultures (such as the United States) vs. managers in diffuse cultures (such as China)?**
Managers in specific cultures separate work and personal lives, compartmentalize their work and private lives, and are open and direct. In diffuse cultures, the manager's work spills over into personal relationships and vice versa. (moderate, page 104)* {AACSB: **Multicultural and Diversity**}

99. **What are the four most common culturally-based variables that may cause problems for Americans in international management?**
Time, change, material factors, and individualism. (moderate, pages 96-97) {AACSB: **Multicultural and Diversity**}

100. **What is the Japanese principle of "wa" and how does it affect Japanese business practices?**
The principle of *wa* means "peace and harmony" and probably originated in the Shinto religion which focuses on spiritual and physical harmony. The principle of *wa* affects Japanese business practices as follows: cooperation in work groups, an emphasis on participative management, consensus problem solving, and decision making with a patient long-term perspective. (moderate, page 111)* {AACSB: **Multicultural and Diversity**}

101. **To what extent has Christianity influenced Germany's culture?**
Over 96% of Germany is Protestant or Catholic. This may be why Germans tend to like rule and order in their lives and why there is a clear public expectation of what is acceptable and what is unacceptable. Public signs in Germany dictate what is forbidden (*verboten*). (difficult, pages 112)* {AACSB: **Multicultural and Diversity**}

102. **What steps can an executive take to develop a cultural profile of a country?**
Managers can gather information from a variety of sources including current research like the work of Hofstede, Trompenaars, and others; personal observations; and discussions with people. This information can be synthesized into a descriptive profile of a country. (moderate, page 109)* {AACSB: **Multicultural and Diversity**}

Comprehensive Essay Questions

103. **Which do you think will have the greater impact on firm performance in a cross-cultural setting: national variables (economic, legal, and political systems) or cultural variables (beliefs, values, and norms)?**
Macro-environmental variables such as economic or political issues are beyond the scope of control of even the most effective manager. Managers can plan their response to such events but can't control them. If companies have done an adequate assessment of country risk factors, then the larger issue becomes that of managing resources in the host country. Once the issue becomes managing resources through people across cultures, then cultural variables will have a greater influence. Further, the way managers interpret the signals and significance of economic, legal, and political events will be through their distinct cultural lenses. Since managers make decisions on what they believe they know, culture plays an import role in issue identification. (difficult, page 92)* {AACSB: **Multicultural and Diversity**}

104. **Research suggests that management teams are superior to individuals in their power to make effective decisions. Given the underlying cultural characteristic of individualism in the U.S., will U.S. firms be able to develop teams that are as strong as those of their foreign competitors?**

Cultures that favor group collectivism or adhesion to the group may be more "naturally equipped" for teamwork. The discussion in the text of the Hofstede work indicates that the output of individuals working in groups differs between individualist and collectivist cultures. In the United States (individualist), for example, social loafing is common and people tend to perform less well in group versus individual settings. One researcher found that the Chinese (collectivist) did not exhibit as much social loafing as Americans since they placed group interests above individual interests. Despite these disadvantages, however, an individualist culture does not doom the U.S. for a number of reasons. First, it is clear that cultural sensitivity can at least in part be learned. This implies that U.S. teams could learn about the collective response of other cultures and the benefit in emulating some parts of it. In terms of U.S. competitors, while their "domestic" culture may be collective, the most successful firms will have to deal cross-culturally. Firms that are naturally team oriented will still have to find ways to integrate individualistic employees from other cultures. Finally, Exhibit 3-6 "Americans at Glance" suggests that Americans are always searching for easier, better ways to accomplish tasks and that traditional American values are in transition which suggests an openness to different cultural approaches.
(difficult, pages 102)* {AACSB: Multicultural and Diversity}

105. **To what extent do you feel national culture is influenced by a country's formal education system?**

Formal education certainly is an influence on national culture, but it is not the only influence. The effect of formal education on cultural values, beliefs, and norms is likely to vary from country to country. For example, countries with strong family-kinship systems (e.g., India) may have less reliance on formal education to convey cultural values. Similarly, countries that have a strong religious orientation (e.g., Saudi Arabia) may place a greater reliance on religious systems to convey values than on formal education. Also, education is only one of eight cultural variables identified in the text. (moderate, page 95-98)* {AACSB: Multicultural and Diversity}

106. **Explain the eight categories that form the subsystems of any society according to Harris and Moran.**

(1) Kinship – a kinship system is the system adopted by a given society to guide family relationships. (2) Education – the formal or informal education of workers in a foreign firm, received from whatever source, greatly affects the expectations placed on those workers in the workplace. (3) Economy – whatever the economic system, the means of production and distribution in a society has a powerful influence on such organizational processes as sourcing, distribution, incentives, and repatriation of capital. (4) Politics – the system of government in a society imposes varying constraints on an organization and its freedom to do business. (5) Religion – the spiritual beliefs of a society are often so powerful that they transcend other cultural aspects. (6) Associations – many and various types of associations arise out of the formal and informal groups that make up a society. (7) Health – the system of health care in a country affects employee productivity, expectations, and attitudes toward physical fitness and its role in the workplace. (8) Recreation – workers' attitudes toward recreation can affect their work behavior and their perception of the role of work in their lives. (difficult, pages 96-89)* {**AACSB: Multicultural and Diversity**}

Chapter 4
Communicating Across Cultures

Multiple Choice Questions

1. The CEO in Taiwan was offended when Mr. Romano called him "Lau-ban ya" instead of "Au-ban" because "Lau-ban ya" meant _____ instead of "No.1 Boss."
    a. Wife of Boss (moderate, page 124)*
    b. Low level employee
    c. Not happy to see you
    d. I wish I had never come here

2. Which of the following does <u>not</u> constitute a normal interpersonal communication task for managers?
    a. coordinate activities
    b. disseminate information
    c. motivate employees
    d. give speeches at conferences (moderate, page 127)

3. Studies by Mintzberg demonstrate that managers spend between _____ percent of their time talking to people.
    a. 10 and 20
    b. 21 and 30
    c. 31 and 40
    e. 50 and 90 (easy, page 126)

4. According to communication researchers Samovar, Porter, and Jain, _____.
    a. cultural factors pervade the communication process (difficult, page 127)
    b. noise is always equally present in cross-cultural communication
    c. culture does not influence with whom we choose to speak
    d. communication behavior is not largely dependent on culture

5. All of the following are part of a person's life space <u>except</u> _____.
    a. culture
    b. experience
    c. values
    d. all of the above (moderate, page 127) {AACSB: Communication}

6.   When a member of one culture sends a message to a member of another culture, _____ takes place.
     a. the value chain
     b. intercultural communication (moderate, page 128) {AACSB: Multicultural and Diversity}
     c. the communication adoption process
     d. homogeneous communication

7.   _____ is the process in which people look for the explanation of another person's behavior.
     a. Attribution (moderate, page 128)
     b. Cultural noise
     c. Stereotyping
     d. Affirmation

8.   According to Hall and Hall, when people in a failed communication blame their confusion on the other person's stupidity, deceit, or craziness, it is an example of _____.
     a. cultural noise
     b. attribution (easy, page 128)*
     c. life space
     d. selective transmission

9.   When there is _____ between the parties, there is less likelihood of miscommunication.
     a. a business relationship
     b. a legal contract
     c. trust (moderate, page 129) {AACSB: Communication}
     d. selective transmission

10. Research by the World Values Study Group shows that _____ had the highest disposition to trust other people.
     a. Nordic countries (difficult, page 129)* {AACSB: Ethical Reasoning}
     b. Japan
     c. United States
     d. African countries

11. According to the GLOBE project, if you were from Sweden, a country ranking low on assertiveness, you would generally prefer _____.
     a. explicitness in communication
     b. a two-way dialogue (easy, page 129)
     c. a contract
     d. cultural noise

12. Which of the following is <u>not</u> a cultural variable in the communication process?
   a. life space (moderate, page 130) {AACSB: Communication}
   b. attitudes
   c. thought patterns
   d. proxemics

13. _____ and _____ are cultural variables in the communication process.
   a. Attitude; ethnicity
   b. Ethnicity; physical appearance
   c. Thought patterns; language (difficult, page 130)
   d. Ethnicity; language

14. If you assume that every member of a society or subculture has the same characteristics or traits, you are guilty of _____.
   a. attribution
   b. stereotyping (easy, page 130)* cultural noise
   c. kinesic behavior

15. The role of the manager _____.
   a. is the same across cultures
   b. varies only slightly across cultures
   c. is the same in nearly all cultures but varies slightly in some cultures
   d. varies widely across cultures (moderate, page 131)

16. Language can be a frequent cause of miscommunication because of _____.
   a. inability to speak or understand the language
   b. poor or too literal translation
   c. missing meaning conveyed through body language
   d. all of the above (easy, page 131)

17. When an Asian says "yes" to your questions he is indicating that _____.
   a. he is in complete agreement with what you say
   b. he has heard you (difficult, page 132)*
   c. he will have to ask his boss
   d. all of the above

18. _____ are elements of nonverbal communication.
   a. Ethnicity and language
   b. Proxemics and ethnicity
   c. Kinesic behavior and proxemics (moderate, page 132)
   d. Language and object language

19.   Posture, gestures, facial expressions, and eye contact are examples of
       _____.
       a. kinesic behavior (easy, page 132)
       b. ningensei
       c. oculesics
       d. noise

20.   Subtle differences in eye behavior are called _____.
       a. proxemics
       b. paralanguage
       c. object language
       d. oculesics (moderate, page 132)

21.   During speech, Americans will look straight at you, but the British keep
       your attention by looking away. This is an example of _____.
       a. oculesics (moderate, page 132)*
       b. proxemics
       c. paralanguage
       d. object language

22.   While in the United States a relaxed posture during a business meeting may
       be accepted, in Europe or Asia it can be construed as _____.
       a. acceptable
       b. bad manners (easy, page 132-133)*
       c. being uninterested in the deal
       d. being ill

23.   Nonverbal communication includes all of the following except _____.
       a. kinesic behavior
       b. proxemics
       c. paralanguage
       d. attributions (moderate, page 132)

24.   Which of the following is not a form of nonverbal communication?
       a. proxemics
       b. paralanguage
       c. object language
       d. word choice (easy, page 132)

25.   Which of the following would likely occur in a high-contact culture?
       a. widening your eyes
       b. looking at your watch
       c. speaking faster
       d. touching while you speak (moderate, page 133) {AACSB: Communication}

26. Which of the following is an example of proxemics?
    a. widening your eyes
    b. moving closer to the listener (moderate, page 133)*
    c. speaking faster
    d. using a translator

27. Which of the following is recognized as a low-contact culture?
    a. Eastern Europeans
    b. Arabs
    c. South Americans
    d. Northern Europeans (moderate, page 133)*

28. Which of the following characteristics is <u>not</u> true of people in a high-contact culture?
    a. prefer to touch a great deal
    b. live in warmer climates
    c. are more individualistic (moderate, page 133)
    d. prefer to stand close

29. If you are from the United States, an individualistic culture, you are more likely to be _____ than say someone from Saudi Arabia which is a collectivist culture.
    a. remote and distant (difficult, page 133)*
    b. touchy and feely
    c. impatient and angry
    d. generous and loud

30. _____ and _____ are elements of paralanguage.
    a. Proxemics; kinesic behavior
    b. Contact; language
    c. Rate of speech; tone of voice (easy, page 133)
    d. All of the above

31. Changing the meaning of words by changing the inflection of your voice is an example of _____.
    a. paralanguage (moderate, page 133)
    b. object language
    c. proxemics

32. The considerable variation between Americans and Chinese in the use of silence in meetings is an aspect of
    a. proxemics
    b. haptics
    c. paralanguage (moderate, page 133)
    d. object language

33. Communicating through architecture, office design and furniture, cars, or cosmetics is an example of _____.
    a. **object language (moderate, page 134)***
    b. oculesics
    c. paralanguage
    d. ningensei

34. Arabs are generally _____.
    a. **high-contact countries (moderate, page 133)***
    b. highly individualistic
    c. encouraging of women's roles in business
    d. low-context cultures

35. Object language is also known as _____.
    a. **material culture (moderate, page 134)**
    b. paralanguage
    c. body language
    d. oculesics

36. Which of the following statements about time systems is true?
    a. Monochronic time systems are linear; polychronic systems have a past, present, and future.
    b. **Monochronic time systems have time experienced in a linear way; polychronic systems have the simultaneous occurrence of many events. (difficult, page 134)***
    c. Monochronic time systems are non-linear; polychronic systems have a past, present, and future.
    d. Monochronic systems have the simultaneous occurrence of many events; polychronic systems are non-linear.

37. Which of the following is not true about monochronic time systems?
    a. They have a past, present, and future.
    b. **They emphasize involvement with people. (difficult, page 134)**
    c. People adhere to time commitments.
    d. People are accustomed to short-term relationships.

38. Which of the following is not true about polychronic time systems?
    a. **Time serves to order life. (difficult, page 134)**
    b. They emphasize involvement with people.
    c. People give priority to relationships over material systems.
    d. People focus on several things at once and are highly distractible.

39. "Time serves to order life" refers to the role of time in _____.
   a. monochronic systems (moderate, page 134)
   b. object language
   c. paralanguage
   d. polychronic systems

40. Which of following is a characteristic of polychronic time systems?
   a. Time serves to order life.
   b. Time is linear.
   c. People adhere to time commitments.
   d. Relationships are more valuable than material systems. (difficult, page 134)

41. Which of the following is not a characteristic of monochronic time systems?
   a. Time is linear.
   b. Time serves to order life.
   c. Time is spent, saved, made up, or wasted.
   d. Relationships are more valuable than material systems. (difficult, page 134)

42. _____ systems tolerate many things occurring simultaneously and emphasize involvement with people.
   a. Polychronic (moderate, page 134)
   b. Monochronic
   c. Paralanguage
   d. Object language

43. All of the following are characteristic of polychronic cultures except _____.
   a. people may be highly distractible
   b. adhering to time commitments (moderate, page 134) {AACSB: Communication}
   c. plans change often
   d. relationships are more valuable than material objects

44. Which of the following is the most accurate statement concerning the role of context in cross-cultural communication?
   a. In high-context cultures the message is implicit; in low-context cultures the message is explicit. (difficult, page 135) {AACSB: Communication}
   b. In high-context cultures there is a low sensory involvement; in low-context cultures there is a high sensory involvement.
   c. In high-context cultures the message is explicit; in low-context cultures the message is implicit.
   d. In high-context cultures there is a high sensory involvement; in low-context cultures there is a low sensory involvement.

45. In high-context cultures _____.
   a. **feelings and thoughts are not explicitly expressed (difficult, page 135) {AACSB: Communication}**
   b. information is readily available
   c. feelings and thoughts are expressed in words
   d. messages are explicit

46. People in _____ cultures expect others to understand unarticulated moods, subtle gestures, and environmental clues that people from _____ cultures simply do not process.
   a. low-context; high-context
   b. low-contact; high-contact
   c. **high-context; low-context (moderate, page 135) {AACSB: Communication}**
   d. monochronic; polychronic

47. Which of the following is considered a high-context culture?
   a. **Asia (easy, page 135)* {AACSB: Communication}**
   b. Germany
   c. Switzerland
   d. Scandinavia

48. In which of the following cultures are personal and business relationships more separated?
   a. high-context cultures
   b. object-context cultures
   c. **low-context cultures (moderate, page 135) {AACSB: Communication}**
   d. cross-context cultures

49. Oriental poker face refers to _____.
   a. the fact that many persons of Far Eastern ancestry play poker in the U.S.
   b. **the inscrutable nature of the facial expression worn by Asians that reflects no particular state of mind (difficult, page 136)***
   c. the perpetual smile worn by many Asians
   d. the regular frown on the face of many Asians

50. In low-context cultures _____.
   a. work and friend relationships are inseparable
   b. feelings and thoughts are not explicitly expressed
   c. one must read between the lines
   d. **feelings and thoughts are expressed in words (difficult, page 135) {AACSB: Communication}**

51. Mr. John Smith carries a scarf as a gift from the United States for the wife of Mr. Ahmed, his business associate in Saudi Arabia. This action will be considered _____.
    a. a friendly gesture on part of the American
    b. an inappropriate and impolite gesture (difficult, page 137)* {AACSB: Communication}
    c. a bribe
    d. an obligation to reciprocate on part of Mr. Ahmed

52. All of the following are part of the concept of ningensei <u>except</u> _____.
    a. high contact (moderate, page 141)* {AACSB: Communication}
    b. reciprocity
    c. receiver orientation
    d. underlying distrust of logic

53. The Japanese preference for humanity, reciprocity and underlying distrust of words and analytic logic is referred to as _____.
    a. kieretsu
    b. ringi-sho
    c. ningensei (difficult, page 141)*
    d. allogato

54. The _____ preference for written communication, even for informal interactions, demonstrates the formality of their relationships.
    a. French (moderate, page 141)* {AACSB: Global, Communication}
    b. German
    c. Arab
    d. Japanese

55. Steps in the development of effective intercultural communication include all of the following <u>except</u> _____.
    a. careful encoding
    b. selective transmission
    c. meaningful attribution (moderate, page 142)
    d. appropriate follow-up

56. Communication over the Internet_____.
    a. is generally unaffected by language, culture, and local laws
    b. must be adjusted to differences in language, culture, and local laws (moderate, page 141)* {AACSB: Use of Information Technology}
    c. will remain dominated by English-language sites in the foreseeable future
    d. a and c only are correct

57. Literal translations are of limited use because _____.
    a. idioms don't mean the same in different languages
    b. they do not include the message sent by body language
    c. there are regional expressions that just don't make sense in translation
    d. all of the above (difficult, page 143) {AACSB: Communication}

58. The best type of medium chosen for a message depends on _____.
    a. the nature of the message
    b. the need for personal interaction
    c. the level of importance of the message
    d. all of the above (easy, page 143) {AACSB: Communication}

59. _____ is the process of translating the received symbols into the interpreted message.
    a. Decoding (easy, page 144) {AACSB: Communication}
    b. Transmitting
    c. Encoding
    d. Fragmenting

60. Respect in communication is conveyed through all of the following <u>except</u>
    _____.
    a. eye contact
    b. body posture
    c. voice tone
    d. gift giving (moderate, page 144) {AACSB: Communication}

61. Interaction posture _____.
    a. occurs in high-context cultures
    b. is the understanding and modeling of local proxemics
    c. is the ability to respond to others in a nonjudgmental way (difficult, page 144)
    d. is the posture used to communicate with Asians

62. Orientation to knowledge _____.
    a. is the ability to respond in a non-judgmental way
    b. is the recognition that one's knowledge is valid for oneself, not others (difficult, page 144)
    c. occurs primarily in high-contact cultures
    d. occurs primarily in low-context cultures

63. According to Kim, _____ and _____ are characteristics of openness.
    a. persistence; resourcefulness
    b. proper orientation to knowledge; internal locus of control
    c. tolerance for ambiguity; extrovertedness (difficult, page 145)
    d. internal locus of control; external locus of control

64. Which of the following according to Kim, are characteristics of openness?
    a. open-mindedness
    b. tolerance for ambiguity
    c. extrovertedness
    d. **all of the above (moderate, page 145)**

65. _____ is the only characteristic shared by both openness in communication and resilience in communication.
    a. **A tolerance for ambiguity (moderate, page 145) {AACSB: Communication}**
    b. Extrovertedness
    c. Resourcefulness
    d. An internal locus of control

Short Essay Questions

66. **What is communication?**
    The process of sharing meaning by transmitting messages through media such as words, behavior, or material artifacts is termed communication. Managers communicate to coordinate activities, to convey information, to motivate people and to make future plans. (easy, page 127) **{AACSB: Communication}**

67. **Describe the elements and importance of a person's life space.**
    A life space is the context of a person's private world and is based largely on culture, experience, relations, and values. Since people filter or selectively understand messages based on their own expectations and perceptions, the more dissimilar the life space between sender and receiver, the greater the noise in the communication process. (moderate, page 127)

68. **How can we reduce noise in cross-cultural communication? Use the steps in the communication process to explain some ways to control noise.**
    Noise can occur at any stage of the communication process: message encoding, the medium, decoding, or feedback. Noise can be reduced at encoding by being sensitive to the cultural differences of the receiver and incorporating knowledge of their culture into the message – this includes minimizing the use of idioms or regional expressions which are difficult to translate. Noise can be reduced by selecting the correct medium for the message. Most important messages should be delivered face to face whenever possible to facilitate the important nonverbal communication process. Decoding requires the receiver to consider the sender's culture as well as his or her own culture in translating the message. Finally, feedback is critical to assure the communication sent was the one received.

However, the same noise that enters the original communication process can also influence the feedback.
(difficult, pages 128, 129, 142-145)* {AACSB: Multicultural and Diversity/Communication}

69. **Why is trust important in communication?**
Effective communication depends on the informal understanding that develops among the parties which is mainly based on trust. In Japan and China for example, business transactions are based on networks of long-standing relationships based on trust rather than formal contracts that are typical in the United States. When there is trust between parties there is implicit understanding between the parties and hence a lesser chance of misunderstanding and miscommunication. (difficult, page 129)* {AACSB: Communication}

70. **List three guidelines that should be followed to cultivate trust among cultures.**
The three guidelines are: (1) create a clear and calculated basis for mutual benefit; (2) improve predictability – strive to resolve conflicts and keep communication open; and (3) develop mutual bonding through regular socializing and friendly contact. (moderate, page 129) {AACSB: Multicultural and Diversity/Communication}

71. **What is nonverbal communication and what forms does it take?**
Nonverbal communication (sometimes referred to as body language) is the encoding and decoding of messages without the use of language. Some forms of nonverbal language are: kinesic behavior, proxemics, paralanguage, and object language. (easy, page 132) {AACSB: Communication}

72. **Describe the cultural variables in the communication process.**
Cultural variables that can influence a person's perceptions have been identified through research. The cultural variables are: attitudes, social organization, thought patterns, roles, language (spoken or written), nonverbal communication (including kinesic behavior, paralanguage, proxemics, and object language), and time. (difficult, page 130)*
{AACSB: Multicultural and Diversity/Communication}

73. **Why is language often a cause of miscommunication across cultures?**
Spoken and written language is a frequent cause of miscommunication stemming from a person's inability to speak the local language or too poor or literal translation, a speaker's failure to explain idioms, or a person missing the meaning conveyed through body language or certain symbols. Even among countries that share the same language, there can be problems in the subtleties and nuances inherent in the use of the language. (moderate, page 131) {AACSB: **Multicultural and Diversity/Communication**}

74. **Describe and compare high-contact and low-contact cultures.**
High contact cultures (e.g., South Americans, Southern and Eastern Europeans, Indonesians, and Arabs) prefer a close sensory involvement – e.g., prefer to stand close and touch a great deal. Low-contact cultures (e.g., North Americans, Asians, and Northern Europeans) prefer less sensory involvement, have a more distant style. (easy, page 133) {AACSB: **Multicultural and Diversity/Communication**}

75. **What are the elements of paralanguage? How are these elements important in cross-cultural communication?**
Paralanguage refers to how something is said rather than the content of what is said. It includes dimensions such as the rate of speech, the tone and inflection of voice, other noises, laughing, or yawning. Paralanguage is important in all cross-cultural communication encounters – it is especially important in high-context cultures. Without an understanding of paralanguage, cultural noise may be induced in the coding, decoding and feedback processes. (moderate, page 133)* {AACSB: **Multicultural and Diversity/Communication**}

76. **Explain the difference between monochronic and polychronic time systems.**
Monochronic time systems (e.g., Switzerland, Germany, and the United States) have a linear system of time with a past, present, and future. People in monochronic systems generally concentrate on one thing at a time. Polychronic time systems (e.g., Latin Americans and Arabs) are a non-linear system of time where people tolerate the simultaneous occurrence of many events. (easy, page 134)

77. **In what ways do different values of time create noise in the communication process?**
The attributions we make concerning time are based on culture. Without knowledge of cultural differences based on values toward time, receivers attribute meaning to messages based on their own values, not those of the senders. For example, in a polychronic system, the sender may allow interruptions or frequent changes in plans which a receiver in a monochronic system might consider rude or unprofessional. (moderate, page 128, 134)*

78. **Describe and compare high-context and low-context cultures.**
In high-context cultures (e.g., Asia, Middle east, Africa, and the Mediterranean), the context in which the communication takes place is vital to the communication of the message – the message is implicit. In low-context cultures (e.g., Germany, Switzerland, Scandinavia, and North America), the context in which the communication takes place is secondary to the communication – the message is explicit.
(moderate, page 135) {**AACSB: Multicultural and Diversity/Communication**}

79. **List five useful guidelines for effective communication for people doing business in the Middle East.**
The guidelines include: (1) be patient; (2) recognize that people and relationships matter more to Arabs than the job, company, or contract; (3) avoid expressing doubts or criticism when others are present; (4) adapt to the norms of body language, flowery speech, and circuitous verbal patterns in the Middle East; and (5) expect many interruptions in meetings, delays in schedules, and changes in plans. (moderate, page 79)* {**AACSB: Multicultural and Diversity/Communication**}

80. **How does the Japanese value of ningensei influence their communication?**
Ningensei is a Japanese concept of communication based on humanity, reciprocity, and a receiver orientation rather than on words or verbal logic. Japanese may encode and decode messages from this framework. As a result, messages that have sound logic but lack a sense of reciprocity or receiver orientation may be rejected. (difficult, page 140-141)* {**AACSB: Multicultural and Diversity/Communication**}

81. **Define decoding and list three main causes of incongruence in the decoding process.**
Decoding is the process of translating the received symbols into the interpreted message. The main causes of incongruence are: (1) the receiver misinterprets the message, (2) the receiver encodes his or her return message incorrectly, or (3) the sender misinterprets the feedback.
(moderate, page 144) {**AACSB: Communication**}

82. **What kinds of personal abilities and behaviors have been shown to facilitate intercultural communication?**
Research has identified seven characteristics that facilitate intercultural communication effectiveness: respect, interaction posture, orientation to knowledge, empathy, interaction management, tolerance for ambiguity, and other-oriented role behavior. (moderate, page 144) {AACSB: Multicultural and Diversity/Communication}

83. **What are the components of intercultural communication effectiveness?**
The seven components are: respect, interaction posture, orientation to knowledge, empathy, interaction management, tolerance for ambiguity, and other-oriented role behavior. (moderate, page 144) {AACSB: Multicultural and Diversity/Communication}

84. **Describe the concept of openness in communication.**
Openness includes traits such as open-mindedness, tolerance for ambiguity, and extrovertedness, all of which facilitate intercultural communication and help the individual adjust to the cross-cultural experience. (moderate, page 145) {AACSB: Communication}

85. **Describe the concept of resilience.**
Resilience is an attribute that helps one achieve cultural adaptation in a cross-cultural context. It includes traits such as having an internal locus of control, persistence, a tolerance for ambiguity, and resourcefulness. (moderate, page 145) {AACSB: Communication}

Comprehensive Essay Questions

86. **Define the concept of proxemics and provide examples of how proxemics differ between the cultures of Asia, Germany, the United States, and France.**
Proxemics deals with the influence of proximity and space on communication, including personal space and office space or layout. Americans expect office layout to provide private space for each person, usually a larger and more private space as one goes up the hierarchy. In much of Asia, the custom is open office space, with people at all levels working and talking in close proximity to one another. Space communicates power in both Germany and the United States, evidenced by the desire for a corner office or one on the top floor. The importance of French officials, however, is made clear by a position in the middle of subordinates, communicating that they have a central position in an information network, where they can stay informed and in control. (moderate, page 133)* {AACSB: Multicultural and Diversity/Communication}

87. **If you were a person from a high-context culture, what problems might you encounter in your first sojourn to a low-context culture?**
You would likely assign meaning (make attributions) about the importance of contextual factors. You would be adding noise by trying to interpret contextual factors that were not intended by the sender to be part of the communication process. You might also feel frustrated at the receiver's inability to understand the messages you were sending by creating a context for your sent messages. In this low-context culture, your receiver is more focused on the message than its context. You might also find it difficult to express thoughts subtly, as you have become used to having the contextual setting partially fulfill that role. (moderate, page 135)*
{AACSB: Multicultural and Diversity/Communication}

Chapter 5
Cross-Cultural Negotiation and Decision Making

Multiple Choice Questions

1. Ignorance of _____, more than any other single factor, accounts for America's unimpressive sales efforts.
    a. native bargaining rituals (moderate, page 153)
    b. domestic industry structure
    c. negotiation strategy
    d. cultural communication processes

2. For long-term positive relations, the goal of negotiation should be
    a. to get the highest possible price for your product or service.
    b. a win-win situation. (moderate, page 153)
    c. a win-lose situation.
    d. not to give in to the other side.

3. A Frenchman assumes that everyone behaves like the French do, assuming projective cognitive similarity. Projective cognitive similarity is _____.
    a. assuming that cognitive information is more important than emotional appeals in negotiating
    b. assuming that others perceive, think, and reason the way you do (difficult, page 153)* {AACSB: Communication}
    c. assuming that people feel they understand you
    d. assuming that people from different cultures negotiate in different ways

4. Which of the following were characteristics of the Chinese negotiating style discussed in the Opening Profile?
    a. difficult to pin down for meetings
    b. difficult to establish a schedule to get the deal done
    c. viewed agreeing to a date as a concession
    d. all of the above (moderate, page 152) {AACSB: Communication}

5. The different stages of the negotiation process are _____.
    a. preparation, relationship building, exchange of task-related information, persuasion, concessions and agreement (difficult, page 154) {AACSB: Communication}
    b. preparation, relationship building, proposal, circulation, approval
    c. relationship building, proposal, exchange of task-related information, persuasion
    d. proposal, circulation, persuasion, approval, record

6.   Which of the following is not a stage of the negotiation process?
      a. preparation
      b. relationship building
      c. persuasion
      **d. all of the above are stages of the negotiation process (easy, page 154)
          {AACSB: Communication}**

7.   To understand differences in negotiating styles of people from other cultures,
      managers first need to understand _____.
      a. the other negotiator's culture
      **b. their own negotiating style (moderate, page 154) {AACSB:
          Communication}**
      c. the five stages of the negotiation process
      d. cognitive versus emotional influences on negotiating success

8.   Prior to the negotiation meetings, managers should find out as much as possible
      about _____.
      a. the kinds of demands that might be made
      b. the composition of the opposing team
      c. the relative authority of the opposing team members
      d. all of the above (easy, pages 154-155) {AACSB: Communication}

9.   All of the following are variables in the negotiation process except _____.
      a. significance of type of issues
      b. concern with protocol
      c. risk-taking propensity
      **d. location of the negotiating sessions (difficult, page 155) {AACSB:
          Communication}**

10.   In many countries, such as Mexico and China, it is personal commitment to
      individuals that form the basis for enforcement of contracts, rather than _____,
      as in America.
      a. information and analysis
      b. scientific research results
      c. the legal system (moderate, page 156)
      d. commitment to the bureaucracy

11.   Participating in social events, tours, ceremonies, and light conversations are
      generally forms of _____.
      a. relationship building (easy, page 156)
      b. information gathering and analysis
      c. conceding to hosts demands
      d. all of the above

12. Which of the following is a bridge from relationship building to the more formal stages of negotiating?
    a. mediating
    b. posturing (moderate, page 156)
    c. conceding
    d. assessing

13. People from _____ tend to put a lot of emphasis on protocol and expect to deal only with top executives.
    a. Japan
    b. Russia (moderate, page 157)*
    c. Europe in general
    d. Latin America in general

14. _____ negotiators enjoy debate and conflict and will often interrupt presentations to argue about an issue even when it has little relevance to the topic being presented.
    a. Italian
    b. Russian
    c. Mexican
    d. French (moderate, page 156)*

15. The opposing negotiating team asks many questions, and delves specifically and repeatedly into details. Most likely you are negotiating with the _____.
    a. Chinese (moderate, page 156)*
    b. Japanese
    c. Mexicans
    d. French

16. According to research by Adler, negotiators should focus not only on presenting their situation and needs, but also on _____.
    a. providing information to the other side
    b. showing an understanding of the other side's viewpoint (difficult, page 157)
    c. avoiding emotional appeals not backed by information
    d. avoiding purely rational approaches to the negotiating process

17. Adler suggests that, to be more effective, negotiators should try to understand the perspectives of both sides and prepare for meetings by practicing _____.
    a. oculesics
    b. proxemics
    c. role reversal (moderate, page 157) {AACSB: Communication}
    d. projective cognitive similarity

18. "Nontask sounding" is most closely associated with which aspect of negotiating?
   a. relationship building (moderate, page 156)
   b. concession granting
   c. information analysis
   d. signing of the final document

19. _____ is described as general polite conversation and informal communication before meetings.
   a. Nontask sounding (moderate, page 156)
   b. Nonverbal behavior
   c. A dirty trick
   d. Role reversal

20. Which group of people is most likely to prefer the use of an intermediary in the negotiating process?
   a. Latin Americans
   b. Middle Easterners (moderate, page 156)*
   c. Americans
   d. Koreans

21. Hard bargaining starts with which phase of the negotiations process?
   a. persuasion (moderate, page 157)
   b. relationship building
   c. information gathering
   d. use of intermediaries

22. According to joint venture research, U.S. executives reported that the behavior of _____ during the course of negotiations was often abusive and resulted in shouting matches.
   a. Chinese
   b. Japanese
   c. Latin Americans
   d. Koreans (moderate, page 157)* {AACSB: Ethical Reasoning}

23. _____ and _____ are common "dirty tricks" in negotiating.
   a. Rudeness; getting down to business quickly
   b. Too-bright lighting; interruptions (moderate, page 157)* {AACSB: Ethical Reasoning}
   c. Uncomfortable room temperatures; asking many questions
   d. Interruptions; keeping silence for a long period

24. All of the following are examples of rough tactics used in negotiations <u>except</u>
    _____.
    a. numerous interruptions
    b. **emotional negotiating style (moderate, page 157) {AACSB: Ethical Reasoning}**
    c. take-it-or-leave-it attitude
    d. physically uncomfortable setting

25. In some South American countries, it is common to start negotiations with
    _____.
    a. high-pressure sales tactics
    b. **misleading or false information (moderate, page 157)* {AACSB: Ethical Reasoning}**
    c. needless delays and ways to waste time
    d. presentation of highly technical information

26. The most subtle behaviors in the negotiation process, and the most difficult to deal with are _____.
    a. communication ploys
    b. **nonverbal messages (moderate, pages 157-158)**
    c. the giving of gifts during entertainment times
    d. defining what technical negotiating terms actually mean

27. According to Graham's study, during a 30-minute negotiating period, Japanese and Americans evidenced no _____ during their negotiating process.
    a. oculesics
    b. emotion
    c. **touching (easy, page 158)* {AACSB: Multicultural and Diversity}**
    d. facial emotions

28. The fifth and last stage of the negotiating process is _____.
    a. analysis and assessment of mutual positions
    b. bargaining and presentation of mutual needs
    c. **concessions and agreement (moderate, page 158)**
    d. mediation and cooperation

29. Research in the United States indicates that the best outcomes are achieved in the agreement phase of negotiating by starting with _____.
    a. **extreme positions (moderate, page 158)**
    b. information
    c. exchange of mutual needs
    d. relationship building

30. Negotiators in the Far East tend to approach issues in what manner?
    a. an indirect manner
    b. a direct manner
    c. a holistic manner (moderate, page 158)*
    d. a linear manner

31. Whereas Americans take contracts very seriously, _____ often renege on their contracts.
    a. French
    b. Russians (easy, page 158)*
    c. Germans
    d. Italians

32. _____ negotiators are very skillful, and usually have spent far more time and effort studying American culture and business practices than Americans have spent studying _____ practices.
    a. German; German
    b. Japanese; Japanese (moderate, page 158)
    c. Russian; Russian
    d. Arabian; Arabian

33. Japanese negotiators are likely to be evasive or even leave the room rather than _____.
    a. be confrontational
    b. be emotional
    c. embarrass the other party
    d. give a direct negative answer (moderate, page 160)

34. Fundamental to the Japanese culture is _____.
    a. hard work and results
    b. treating people in informal ways
    c. the welfare of the group (moderate, page 160)*
    d. the welfare of the individual

35. _____ are based on what people believe is objective information, presented with the assumption that it is understood by the other side on a logical basis.
    a. Factual appeals (moderate, page 160)
    b. Affective appeals
    c. Axiomatic appeals
    d. Virtual appeals

36. Which of the following types of appeals is based on emotions and subjective feelings?
   a. factual appeals
   b. affective appeals (moderate, page 160)
   c. axiomatic appeals
   d. virtual appeals

37. Axiomatic appeals are based on _____.
   a. socially accepted ideals (moderate, page 160) {AACSB: Ethical Reasoning}
   b. quantified information
   c. non-emotional analysis
   d. emotional analysis backed by information

38. One of the most common tough negotiating tactics used by Russians is _____.
   a. calling Americans dishonest
   b. ridiculing information provided by American negotiators
   c. stalling for time and haggling (moderate, page 160)*
   d. faking emotion

39. In contrast to Russians, Arabs are more likely to make concessions because of their interest in _____.
   a. compromise
   b. accommodating the needs of others
   c. long-term relationships (moderate, page 160)* {AACSB: Multicultural and Diversity}
   d. financial negotiating variables

40. According to Casse, the successful American negotiator (as perceived by fellow Americans) does all of the following in his or her home country except _____.
   a. knows when to compromise
   b. engages in relationship building (moderate, page 160)
   c. operates in good faith
   d. has a sense of timing

41. Which of the following is inconsistent with the cultural profile of a successful American negotiator (as perceived by fellow Americans)?
   a. Keeps cards close to the chest
   b. Has a good sense of timing and is consistent
   c. Very quiet and thoughtful (difficult, page 160)
   d. Takes a firm stand at the beginning of the negotiation

42. Which of the following are characteristics of successful Indian negotiators (as perceived by fellow Indians)?
    a. Looks for and says the truth
    b. Is not afraid of speaking up and has no fears
    c. Exercises self-control
    d. **all of the above (moderate, page 161)***

43. Arab negotiators _____.
    a. use affective appeals based on emotions and subjective feelings
    b. are more interested in long-term relationships
    c. are more likely to make concessions
    d. **all of the above (moderate, page 160)***

44. According to Casse's profiles, _____ negotiators are very quiet and thoughtful, factual, straightforward, extremely polite, and punctual.
    a. American
    b. **Swedish (difficult, page 160)***
    c. Chinese
    d. Korean

45. The _____ is the nature and the appearance of the relationship between the pursuing common goals.
    a. **software of negotiation (moderate, page 164)**
    b. hardware of negotiation
    c. objectivity of negotiation
    d. transparency of negotiation

46. Husted's study found that many culture-based differences in negotiation reflected differences between_____.
    a. rich vs. poor countries
    b. aggressive vs. passive individuals
    c. **high vs. low-context cultures (moderate, pages 164-165)***
    d. male vs. female negotiators

47. Skillful negotiators tend to make twice as many comments regarding _____ than less skillful negotiators.
    a. short-term issues
    b. non-financial issues
    c. marketing issues
    d. **long-term issues (moderate, page 166)**

48. Negotiators report two major areas of conflict in negotiating with the Chinese –
their apparent insincerity about reaching an agreement and _____.
    a. their unwillingness to develop relationships beyond a superficial level
    b. their insistence on compromise whenever the going gets tough
    **c. the amount of detail desired about product characteristics (difficult,
        page 168)***
    d. their use of bureaucratic mechanisms to stall

49. Which of the following is not considered an antecedent factor that has
influences on Western-Chinese business negotiations?
    a. etiquette
    b. harmony
    c. economic conditions
    d. personality (difficult, page 168)*

50. In negotiating with the Chinese, appeals to _____ will probably backfire.
    **a. individual members of the Chinese negotiating team (moderate, page
        169)***
    b. the group as a whole
    c. the need for compromise
    d. the need for more time

51. "Guanxi" means _____.
    a. productivity
    b. understanding between peers
    c. intricate, pervasive network of personal relations (moderate, page 169)
    d. unacceptable negotiating tactics

52. What are the two negotiation stages Americans often experience with the
Chinese?
    a. informational and emotional
    b. ceremonial and technical
    c. commercial and societal
    d. technical and commercial (moderate, page 170)

53. In negotiating with the Chinese, you can expect to spend about a third of your
time discussing technical specifications another third on price negotiations and
the rest on _____.
    a. entertainment-related concerns
    b. price negotiations
    c. general negotiations and posturing (moderate, page 170)
    d. all of the above

54. _____ are considered to be among the toughest negotiators in the world.
   a. Americans
   b. Latin Americans
   c. Germans
   d. Chinese (moderate, page 170)*

55. The Chinese often put pressure on Americans in the negotiation process by
   _____.
   a. driving a hard bargain with respect to price
   **b. "shaming" them, implying that Americans are reneging on the
       friendship (moderate, page 170)**
   c. refusing to compromise
   d. asking for concessions relating to product delivery time

56. The best kind of negotiator to send to China is _____.
   a. someone experienced in technical negotiations
   b. someone older and more experienced (moderate, page 170)
   c. patient people who are willing to drive a hard bargain and not make many
       concessions
   d. someone who understands the meaning of compromise

57. Which of the following is not considered a good tip to foreigners conducting
   business with the Chinese?
   a. Avoid giving gifts as tokens of friendship. (easy, page 170)
   b. Accept prolonged periods of stalemate.
   c. Refrain from exaggerated expectations.
   d. Expect the Chinese will try to manipulate by shaming.

58. The _____ approach to conflict tends to deal on the basis of factual information
   and logical analysis.
   a. instrumental-oriented (moderate, page 171)
   b. expressive-oriented
   c. affective-oriented
   d. subjective-oriented

59. Which of the following approaches to conflict handles a situation indirectly and
   implicitly and also does not have a delineation of the situation from the person
   handling it?
   a. instrumental-oriented
   b. expressive-oriented (moderate, page 171) {AACSB: Communication}
   c. objective-oriented
   d. axiomatic-oriented

60. Which of the following is <u>not</u> a step in the decision-making process?
   a. Define the problem.
   b. Gather and analyze relevant data.
   c. Consider alternative solutions.
   d. Gather feedback from subordinates. (moderate, page 172)

61. Research shows that American managers have the highest _____, a cultural variable that greatly influences decision-making.
   a. tolerance for risk (difficult, page 172) {AACSB: Multicultural and Diversity
   b. success with negotiation
   c. amount of patience
   d. all of the above

62. American managers tend to exhibit more of which of the following characteristic than their foreign counterparts?
   a. external locus of control
   b. diffused locus of control
   c. internal locus of control (moderate, page 172) {AACSB: Multicultural and Diversity
   d. body language

63. In China, which is a highly collectivist society, employees expect _____ because their value system presupposes the superior to be automatically the most wise.
   a. participative leadership
   b. autocratic leadership (moderate, page 173)* {AACSB: Multicultural and Diversity
   c. democratic leadership
   d. None of the answers is correct.

64. The "ringi-sho" is the _____.
   a. primary negotiator for the Japanese team
   b. highest ranking member of a Japanese negotiating team
   c. final written document produced in the decision-making process
   d. original written proposal (moderate, page 175)*

65. The culture of _____ and _____ underlies the Japanese "ringi" system of decision making.
   a. collectivism; shared responsibility (moderate, page 174)
   b. obedience; loyalty
   c. authoritarianism; devotion
   d. individual responsibility; lifetime employment

66. The four stages of the ringi system are _____.
    a. preparation, relationship building, exchange of task-related information, persuasion
    b. proposal, circulation, approval, record (difficult, page 175)
    c. preparation, relationship building, proposal, circulation
    d. relationship building, exchange of task-related information, persuasion, circulation

67. Mr. Arif Masood Naqui, chief executive of Abraag Capital_____.
    a. wants to create a one-stop financial services shop offering services in lending, investment banking, and brokerage
    b. will focus on the Middle East and southeast Asia
    c. recognizes opportunities for deal makers and investors in the Middle East
    d. all of the above (moderate, pages 163-164)

Short Essay Questions

68. **Explain the problem of "projective cognitive similarity" in cross-cultural negotiations.**
    Projective cognitive similarity refers to the common practice of assuming that those you are negotiating with perceive, judge, think, and reason in the same way when in reality they do not because of different cultural values. Successful negotiators will empathize with their counterparts and share their own viewpoint. (moderate, page 153) {**AACSB: Multicultural and Diversity**}

69. **Define negotiation. Why is it a complex activity?**
    The word negotiation describes the process of discussion between two or more parties aimed at reaching a mutually acceptable agreement. The goal of successful negotiation should be to benefit all parties involved. It is a complex activity especially in the international context because of differences in cultural values, lifestyles, expectations, and verbal and nonverbal language, approaches to formal procedures, and problem-solving techniques. Due to the high number of stakeholders involved in international negotiations, the task becomes very complicated. (moderate, page 153)

70. **List the five stages of the negotiation process?**
    Preparation, relationship building, exchange of task-related information, persuasion, and concessions and agreements. (moderate, page 154)

71. **Why is relationship building so important to negotiating in many cultures around the world?**

Relationship building and nontask sounding is very important in the negotiation process because many cultures prefer to do business with the person rather than with the company or the system. Foreign negotiators want to build trust and respect as a basis for negotiating contracts and take time to patiently develop a mutually trusting relationship. (moderate, page 156) {AACSB: **Multicultural and Diversity**}

72. **Discuss the importance of nonverbal communication in the negotiation process.**

The most subtle behaviors in the negotiation process, and often the most difficult to deal with, are usually the nonverbal messages—the use of voice intonation, facial and body expressions, eye contact, dress, and the timing of the discussion. Nonverbal behaviors are ingrained aspects of culture used by people in their daily lives; they are not specifically changed for the purposes of negotiation. (moderate, pages 157-158)*

73. **Many Asian cultures have a more holistic approach than their Western counterparts. How might this holistic approach affect their negotiation process?**

A holistic approach may not require very lengthy and detailed negotiations. You will not need to deconstruct a problem into a set of small issues, reach agreement on each small issue, and then assume that you have reached agreement on the larger negotiation agenda. The discussions will be more wide ranging and may hold promise for future long term relationships. Negotiators in the Far East, for example, approach negotiation in a holistic way, deciding on the whole deal at the end, rather than making incremental concessions (moderate, page 158)* {AACSB: **Multicultural and Diversity**}

74. **How should you respond in negotiations if the other side begins to employ "dirty tricks"?**

Common dirty tricks include such things as rudeness, overly bright lighting, uncomfortable room temperatures, and interruptions. It is valuable to remember that dirty tricks are more common in some cultures. It is important to not let the dirty tricks impede your negotiations. One technique that might be valuable is to rehearse or role-play your negotiation in a context filled with dirty tricks. By the time you reach the actual negotiation, you will likely be indifferent to their effects. Another approach is to reach an agreement prior to the task negotiations on the negotiation process (issues like creature comfort, interruptions, and lighting can be agreed to in advance). (moderate, pages 157-158)* {AACSB: **Ethical Reasoning**}

75. **List some of the most common rough tactics in negotiating.**
Some of the common dirty tricks include making people physically uncomfortable by raising or lowering the temperature too much, having overly bright lighting, causing numerous interruptions; causing psychological stress; making widespread use of calculated delays; and displaying a take-it-or-leave-it attitude. (moderate, page 157) {AACSB: **Ethical Reasoning**}

76. **What is the purpose of nontask sounding?**
Nontask sounding attempts to build relationships before the hard bargaining begins. This is an important stage in many cultures in the trust building process. (moderate, page 156)

77. **Why do the Japanese tend to be calm, quiet, patient negotiators?**
The Japanese place strong emphasis on harmony, duty, face-saving, and long-term relationships across the board. They are accustomed to long, detailed negotiating sessions. Because the Japanese prefer to develop long term, personal relationships, they will spend more time in nontask sounding. (moderate, page 159-160)* {AACSB: **Multicultural and Diversity**}

78. **How are appeals structured differently in different cultures?**
Americans tend to appeal to logic, ensuing factual appeals. Another approach, favored by Arabs, is to appeal to emotions with an affective appeal. A third approach, one used by Russians, is an axiomatic approach – appeals made to common or generally accepted ideals in their culture. (moderate, page 160)* {AACSB: **Multicultural and Diversity**}

79. **Characterize the typical style of American negotiation.**
An American negotiator gets down to business rapidly; is more rational than emotional; gives little attention to relationship building; respects opponents keeps cards close to his chest; and is very time conscious. (moderate, page 159-160)*

80. **Modern technology can provide support for the negotiating process. List three ways in which negotiation support systems can provide support for the negotiation process.**
(1) Increase the likelihood that an agreement is reached when a zone of agreement exists; (2) decrease the direct and indirect costs of negotiations; and (3) maximize the chances for optimal outcomes. (moderate, page 166) {AACSB: **Uses of Information Technology**}

81. **What are some of the practices used by successful negotiators in their planning and face-to-face behavior based on work by the Huthwaite Research Group?**
During planning, successful negotiators consider a wider range of options, and tend to make twice as many comments regarding long-term issues. In face-to-face behavior, successful negotiators make fewer irritating comments (such as "We're making you a generous offer"), make fewer counterproposals, and use fewer reasons to back up arguments. In addition, skilled negotiators practice active listening. (difficult, page 166)

82. **Give an example of internal and external locus of control.**
Some managers feel that they can plan on certain outcomes because they are in control of events that will direct the future in the desired way. This is called internal locus of control. In contrast, other managers believe that such decisions are of no value because they have little control over the future which lies in the hands of outside forces such as fate, God, or nature. This is called external locus of control. American managers function with an internal locus of control whereas managers in many other countries such as Indonesia and Malaysia do not believe they have as much control over events. (moderate, pages 172-173)*

83. **Describe the process of decision making common in Japanese companies.**
Japanese decision making is a very participative process, characterized by an elaborate and formal system for achieving consensus and agreement among everyone affected by a particular decision. This system, called the ringi system, works from the bottom up in contrast with the American centralized decision making process, which takes a top-down approach. The ringi process consists of four steps: proposal, circulation, approval, and record. (moderate, pages 174-175) **{AACSB: Multicultural and Diversity}**

Comprehensive Essay Questions

84. **List and discuss at least six variables in the negotiation process.**
    a. Basic conception of negotiation process: Is it a competitive process or a problem-solving approach?
    b. Negotiator selection criteria: Is selection based on experience, status, expertise, personal attributes, or some other characteristic?
    c. Significance of type of issue: Is it specific or is the focus on relationships or the format of talks?
    d. Concern with protocol: What is the importance of procedures in the negotiation process?
    e. Complexity of communicative context: What degree of reliance is placed on nonverbal cues to interpret information?
    f. Nature of persuasive arguments: How do the parties attempt to influence each other?
    g. Role of individuals' aspirations: Are motivations based on individual, company, or community goals?
    h. Bases of trust: Is trust based on past experience, intuition, or rules?
    i. Risk-taking propensity: How much do the parties try to avoid uncertainty in trading information?
    j. Value of time: What is each party's attitude toward time?
    k. Decision-making system: How does each team reach decisions—by individual determination, by majority opinion, or by group consensus?
    l. Form of satisfactory agreement: Is agreement based on trust, the credibility of the parties, commitment, or a legally binding contract? (difficult, page 155) {**AACSB: Communication**}

85. **In what ways might the American style of negotiation be misinterpreted in another culture?**
    The American's desire to get down to business quickly might be interpreted as a lack of concern for rigorous process or a lack of concern for relationship building. The American rational (unemotional) style might be misperceived as showing a lack of commitment. The emphasis on time might misinterpreted as a rough tactic – attempting to pressure the other team into making a decision too quickly or before consensus has been reached. (moderate, pages 154-160) {**AACSB: Multicultural and Diversity**}

86. **Assume you are negotiating with a Chinese professor about a grade you received. How should you adjust your negotiation style?**
First, realize that the effect of cultural characteristics on negotiation style is not deterministic. The guidelines given are broad, and individual members of a particular culture should not be expected to adhere to all aspects of a negotiating style. Thus, what you have learned in this chapter would only provide a general guideline to likely behavior by the professor. The Chinese professor might tend to want lots of detailed information about the issues. The student's claims will need to de documented. The professor is likely to be emotionally restrained, and emotional outbursts from the student me will hurt his cause. The professor's facial expressions might be hard to read; and he would likely stress long-term, trusting relationships. (moderate, pages 167-170)* {**AACSB: Multicultural and Diversity**}

87. **Assume you are with a Japanese firm that has just acquired a U.S. company. You wish to institute a ringi decision process in your new subsidiary. What difficulties might you encounter?**
The ringi process consists of four steps: proposal, circulation, approval, and record. The system is rather elaborate and formal. A goal of the system is to achieve consensus among everyone affected by a particular decision. The U.S. system does not require consensus. Managers are allowed to make more centralized decisions and act more autocratically than their Japanese counterparts. The U.S. managers may make incorrect attributions about the Japanese process. They may perceive their new managers as indecisive. They may feel it takes too long to reach a decision. As a result, they may feel the company is being poorly managed or even unmanaged. (moderate, pages 175-175)* {**AACSB: Multicultural and Diversity**}

Chapter 6
Formulating Strategy

Multiple Choice Questions

1. Which of the following was not one of Wal Mart's missteps?
   a. The acquisition of Asda, Britain's number one discount chain in 1999. (moderate, page 207)
   b. Selling packaged meat in Germany.
   c. Selling golf clubs in Brazil.
   d. Selling skates in Mexico.

2. Which of the following practices explain Wal Mart's problems in international expansion?
   a. Low prices, good inventory control, and a large array of merchandise did not work in some countries.
   b. Requiring sales clerks in Germany to smile at customers.
   c. Requiring executives at its German headquarters to move to a new location.
   d. All of the above. (moderate, pages 203-206)

3. The top two recipients in Foreign Direct Investment (FDI) in 2005 were_____.
   a. United Kingdom, United States (moderate, page 207)*
   b. France, Germany
   c. Spain, Italy
   d. Netherlands, Canada

4. The process by which a firm's managers evaluate the future prospects of the firm and decide on appropriate strategies to achieve long-term objectives is called _____.
   a. strategic planning (moderate, page 208)
   b. internal resource analysis
   c. environmental scanning
   d. product planning

5. The basic means by which a company competes — its choice of business in which to operate and the ways in which it differentiates itself from its competitors — is called its _____.
   a. policy
   b. procedure
   c. strategy (easy, page 208)
   d. process

6. Management consultant Ram Charan advises that the "seismic change" to the competitive landscape has been brought about by_____and_____.
   a. globalization, the Internet (moderate, page 208)
   b. terrorism, technology
   c. trade, investment
   d. MNCs, SMEs

7. Europe is currently attracting much new investment capital because of_____.
   a. low labor costs in Europe
   b. the opening of new markets in Eastern Europe (difficult, page 209)
   c. lack of new investment opportunities in Asia
   d. lack of new investment opportunities in North America

8. _____ can be considered a reactive reason for a firm going international.
   a. Globalization of competitors (easy, page 209)
   b. Economies of scale
   c. Cost savings
   d. all of the above

9. Which of the following can be considered to be trade barriers that companies seek to overcome by going international?
   a. tariffs
   b. quotas
   c. buy-local policies
   d. all of the above (easy, page 209)

10. The U.S. pharmaceutical maker SmithKline and Britain's Beecham merged for what primary reason?
    a. to pursue new customer demands
    b. for economy of scale reasons
    c. because of limited domestic expansion opportunities
    d. to avoid licensing and regulatory hassles in their largest markets (difficult, pages 210-211)*

11. To _____ is a proactive reason that prompts a company to go overseas.
    a. get around restrictive trade barriers
    b. respond to new emerging consumer demands
    c. respond to the moves of its foreign competitors
    d. seek economies of scale (difficult, page 210)

12. _____ and _____ are two proactive reasons for a firm going international.
    a. International competition; trade barriers
    b. Trade barriers; economies of scale
    c. Economies of scale; government incentives (difficult, pages 210-212)
    d. all of the above

13. The high costs of research and development, such as in the pharmaceutical industry, along with the cost of keeping up with new technologies, can often be recouped only through _____.
   a. domestic competition
   b. high tariffs
   c. global sales (moderate, page 210)* {AACSB: Uses of Information Technology}
   d. government subsidies

14. What is perhaps the most likely reason why McDonald's has aggressively expanded internationally?
   a. to cut costs
   b. to find new sources of financing
   c. to overcome limited expansion opportunities at home (moderate, page 210)*
   d. to establish economies of scale

15. Avon's marketing strategy of house to house calls saw a decline in the United States mainly because_____.
   a. many homes are empty during the day because of women working outside their homes (moderate, page 210)*
   b. women are reluctant to allow strangers in their home
   c. many communities in America are gated and do not allow Avon ladies
   d. the number of households in the US has grown tremendously.

16. Governments often attract foreign investment by providing incentives such as _____.
   a. use of property
   b. reduced taxes or tax holidays
   c. subsidies
   d. all of the above (easy, page 212)

17. When Disney went to Paris, the French Government gave Disney prime farm land just outside of Paris. According to the text, Disney was proactive because it was _____.
   a. accessing resources that may not be available in home country (moderate, page 212)*
   b. overcoming trade barriers
   c. following the competition
   d. all of the above

18. When Cemex, the Mexican cement giant, acquired several foreign companies and integrated them into Cemex, it was taking advantage of_____.
    a. growth opportunities (moderate, page 211)
    b. economies of scale
    c. reduced trade barriers
    d. government incentives

19. All of the following statements about strategic planning are true except:
    a. companies define or clarify missions before they assess the external environment
    b. once a strategic plan is made, it is never changed (difficult, pages 212-213)
    c. internal strengths are assessed prior to the generation of strategic alternatives
    d. threats and opportunities are usually assessed before strengths and weaknesses

20. The planning phase of the strategic process consists of all of the following except _____.
    a. clarifying mission
    b. establishing an organizational structure (moderate, pages 212-213)
    c. assessing the external environment
    d. performing a SWOT analysis

21. _____ charts the direction of the company and provides a basis for strategic decision making.
    a. Environmental assessment
    b. External analysis
    c. The mission (moderate, page 214)
    d. SWOT analysis

22. Which category is not typically included among global corporate objectives?
    a. research and development
    b. entrepreneurship (moderate, page 214)
    c. profitability
    d. production

23. Goals for market volume and profitability are usually set higher for international than domestic operations because _____.
    a. there is greater risk involved (moderate, page 214)
    b. the market is larger
    c. the company wants to expand
    d. the taxes to be paid are higher

24. After clarification of corporate mission and objectives, the first major step in weighing international strategic options is _____.
    a. political instability analysis
    b. SWOT analysis
    c. environmental assessment (moderate, page 214)
    d. mission assessment

25. _____ and _____ are examples of financial global corporate objectives.
    a. Foreign-exchange management; optimum capital structure (difficult, page 214)
    b. Level of profits; financing of foreign affiliates
    c. Level of profits; growth in sales
    d. Growth in sales; market share

26. _____ as a variable represents a volatile and uncontrollable risk to MNC who must carefully assess such risk as it may result in loss of profitability and even ownership.
    a. Political instability (moderate, page 215)
    b. Tax savings
    c. Raising cheap loans
    d. all of the above

27. Import controls, equity requirements, and local content requirements are all examples of _____.
    a. currency instability
    b. political instability
    c. nationalism (difficult, page 215)*
    d. protective barriers against domestic firms

28. Which of the following environmental scanning variables represents the home government's goals for independence and economic improvement and often influences foreign companies?
    a. political instability
    b. currency instability
    c. nationalism (moderate, page 215)
    d. international competition

29. Environmental scanning should cover all of the following major variables except _____.
    a. political instability
    b. currency instability
    c. international competition
    d. all of the above should be covered (moderate, page 215)

30. _____ is the most important area for environmental assessment and strategy formulation.
   a. SWOT analysis
   b. Cost benefit analysis
   c. Industry analysis (the diamond model)
   d. Global competitor analysis (difficult, page 215)

31. Firms should perform global environmental analysis at which three levels?
   a. product, industry, market
   b. multinational, regional, and local (moderate, page 215)
   c. bargaining power of buyers, suppliers, and rivals
   d. factor conditions, demand conditions, and industry structure

32. The first broad scan of all potential world markets should result in the firm being able to _____.
   a. determine where it will operate
   b. eliminate markets that are closed or insignificant (difficult, page 216)*
   c. identify its most serious competitors
   d. identify the strengths and weaknesses of its competitors

33. Mitsubishi Trading Company employs over 60,000 people whose job is to _____.
   a. develop new technology
   b. form joint ventures abroad
   c. gather, analyze, and feed market information to the parent company (moderate, page 217)*
   d. find ways to develop new technology in new markets

34. Internal sources of information help eliminate unreliable information from secondary sources, particularly in _____.
   a. developing countries (easy, page 217)
   b. technologically advanced countries
   c. countries participating in joint ventures
   d. countries that have governmentally-controlled economies

35. The internal analysis focuses on the company's _____.
   a. mission
   b. past strategy
   c. future strategy
   d. resources and operations (moderate, page 217)

36. _____ is (are) diagnostic tool(s) available to the a company to conduct an internal resource audit.
    a. Financial ratios
    b. Sales force analysis
    c. Both a and b (easy, page 217)
    d. Neither a nor b

37. Operational issues to be taken into account by companies wanting to start or improve international ventures could be_____.
    a. difficulty of obtaining marketing information in many countries
    b. poorly developed financial markets
    c. complexities of exchanges rates and government controls
    d. all of the above (moderate, page 217)

38. A key success factor for Wal Mart is _____.
    a. capacity to miniaturize
    b. new product development
    c. effective sourcing, and distribution channels (moderate, page 217)*
    d. electronic precision

39. The third stage of the strategic planning process is _____.
    a. SWOT analysis (easy, page 218)
    b. environmental analysis
    c. formulation of core competencies
    d. industry analysis

40. The core competencies of a company involve its _____.
    a. key weaknesses and threats
    b. mission and purpose
    c. key customer groups
    d. key strengths (moderate, page 218)

41. The core competency of the Philips Corporation is _____.
    a. electronics
    b. optical media expertise (moderate, page 218)*
    c. miniaturization
    d. new product development

42. Political risk, trade barriers, and regulatory risk are part of the _____model.
    a. industry-based
    b. resource-based
    c. institutional-based (easy, page 218)
    d. strategy-based

43. _____ is a term that refers to the establishment of worldwide operations and the development of standardized products and marketing.
    a. Customization
    b. **Globalization (easy, pages 220-221)**
    c. Nationalization
    d. Internationalization

44. All of the following are examples of pressures to globalize except _____.
    a. increasing competitive clout resulting from regional trading blocs
    b. declining tariffs, which encourage trading across borders and open up new markets
    c. the information technology explosion, which increases the commonality of consumer tastes
    d. **all of the selections are correct (difficult, page 221)***

45. One of the quickest and cheapest ways to develop a global strategy is through _____.
    a. exporting
    b. wholly owned subsidiaries
    c. **strategic alliances (easy, page 221)**
    d. importing

46. Research by Morrison, Ricks, and Roth found that _____ was often a more manageable and less risky strategy than globalization.
    a. joint ventures
    b. **regionalization/localization (moderate, page 221)**
    c. exporting
    d. importing

47. Regional strategies are more appropriate than global strategies for firms which operate in what kind of situation?
    a. **multi-domestic industries (moderate, page 221)***
    b. high-tech industries
    c. newly emerging industries
    d. mature industries, which have been in existence for several decades

48. Which of the following is/ are pressure(s) to localize?
    a. unique consumer preference resulting from cultural or national differences
    b. domestic subsidies
    c. new technologies that allow product variation at a cheaper cost than before
    d. **all of the above (easy, page 222)**

49. Dell, with its worldwide sourcing and fully integrated production and marketing system is considered to be_____.
   a. a multidomestic company
   b. a regional company
   c. a fully local company
   d. a globally integrated company (easy, page 222)

50. Fuji-Xerox and Broken Hill Proprietary are examples of companies that are
   a. moving more towards a multidomestic strategy.
   b. moving rapidly into e-business. (moderate, page 223)*
   c. scaling back their international operations.
   d. focusing primarily on exporting.

51. eBay is an example of a firm that has embarked on a
   a. local e-strategy
   b. regional e-strategy.
   c. multidomestic e-strategy.
   d. global e-strategy (easy, page 224)*

52. Under which of the following conditions is the e-local approach preferable?
   a. when production and consumption are regional rather than global in scope
   b. when customer behavior and market structures differ across regions but are relatively similar within a region
   c. when supply-chain management is very important to success
   d. all of the selections are correct (difficult, page 225)

53. Which of the following is generally the least risky strategy?
   a. franchising
   b. joint ventures
   c. exporting (easy, page 225)
   d. fully owned subsidiaries

54. Small firms seldom go beyond what stage of strategy?
   a. contract manufacturing
   b. exporting (easy, page 225)
   c. turnkey projects
   d. joint ventures

55. Which of the following is a critical environmental factor that needs to be considered when exporting?
   a. export - import tariffs and quotas
   b. freight costs
   c. distance from supplier countries
   d. all of the above (easy, page 226)

56. The licensing strategy is especially suitable for what situation?
    a. the mature phase of the product life cycle (moderate, page 226)
    b. newly emerging industries
    c. high-tech products
    d. services

57. Under which condition is the licensing strategy generally <u>not</u> appropriate?
    a. for firms with diverse product lines
    b. for firms with many financial and managerial resources (moderate, page 220)
    c. when competition is intense
    d. for firms with rapidly changing technology

58. Which of the following is <u>not</u> an advantage of using a licensing agreement?
    a. Licensing avoids the tariffs and quotas usually imposed on exports.
    b. A licensor has total control over the licensee's performance. (moderate, page 226)*
    c. Licensing is a relatively low-risk strategy because it requires little investment.
    d. Licensing is especially suitable for the mature phase of a product's life cycle.

59. The critical criterion in the use of a franchising strategy is _____.
    a. the franchisor's financial reserve
    b. the franchisor's quality of management
    c. quality control (moderate, page 226)
    d. whether or not the local market has sophisticated consumers

60. The primary motive in the contract manufacturing strategy generally is _____.
    a. utilizing cheaper labor overseas (difficult, page 226)*
    b. obtaining rights to patented technology
    c. sharing managerial expertise
    d. sharing financial resources

61. Which of the following is an example of service sector outsourcing jobs?
    a. call center jobs
    b. software design
    c. insurance claims processing
    d. all of the above (easy, page 227)*

62. When a knowledge worker in India designs chips for Intel, it is an example of
    _____.
    a. franchising
    b. licensing
    c. service sector outsourcing (easy, page 227)*
    d. importing

63. A country that has highly qualified technical workers and has benefited from service sector outsourcing from the U.S. is _____.
    a. Nigeria
    b. Iceland
    c. Japan
    d. **India (easy, page 227)***

64. In a _____, a company designs and constructs a facility abroad, trains local personnel, and then turns the key over to local management for a fee.
    a. franchise
    b. management contract
    c. **turnkey operation (moderate, page 228)**
    d. contract manufacturing agreement

65. When the Italian company Fiat constructed an automobile plant in the former Soviet Union, it was an example of _____.
    a. exporting
    b. joint venture
    c. **a turnkey operation (easy, page 228)***
    d. a wholly owned subsidiary

66. A _____ gives a foreign company the rights to manage the daily operations of a business but not to make decisions regarding ownership, financing, or strategy and policy changes.
    a. franchise
    b. **management contract (moderate, page 228)**
    c. turnkey operation
    d. contract manufacturing agreement

67. Which of the following strategies is more likely to be a short-term strategy only?
    a. joint venture
    b. **management contract (moderate, page 228)**
    c. contract manufacturing
    d. licensing

68. Which of the following companies is recognized as using turnkey operations as an entry strategy alternative?
    a. McDonald's
    b. **Fiat (moderate, page 228)***
    c. KFC
    d. Disney

69. Which of the following strategies would most likely be used by a non-European company wanting to gain quick entry inside the European community?
   a. International joint venture (moderate, pages 228-229)
   b. management contract
   c. turnkey operation
   d. franchising

70. More than half of international joint ventures fail due to _____.
   a. poor partner selection
   b. ineffective managerial decisions regarding type of joint venture
   c. insufficient attention to need for preparation and cooperation
   d. all of the above (easy, page 229)

71. Which of the following is generally the most risky strategy?
   a. fully owned subsidiaries (easy, page 229)
   b. franchising
   c. joint ventures
   d. contract manufacturing

72. The cost of operating a subsidiary in EU is high because of _____.
   a. high labor costs
   b. high taxation
   c. harmonization codes that have to be adhered to
   d. all of the above (difficult, pages 233-234)*

73. MNCs that have a subsidiary in EU but based in non EU country, sometimes have an advantage because of _____.
   a. superior competitiveness and research and development
   b. an existing foothold in the market
   c. reduced operating expenses as you need to have just one subsidiary for all of EU
   d. all of the above (difficult, page 233)

74. _____ and _____ are examples of location factors in entry mode planning.
   a. Country risk; cultural distance (difficult, page 234)
   b. Size of planned venture; knowledge of local market
   c. Industry growth rate; potential of local market
   d. International experience; competition in local market

75. According to Gupta and Govindrajan, which factor is taken into account when deciding on an alliance based strategy?
   a. available capital
   b. government regulations
   c. cultural distance between home and host countries
   d. all of the above (easy, pages 234, 236)

Short Essay Questions

76. **Define strategy and explain the strategic planning process.**
    Strategy is the basic means by which a company competes, including the choice of business or businesses in which to operate and the ways to differentiate itself from competitors in those businesses. The strategic planning process involves establishing the mission and objectives of the firm, assessing environmental factors, conducting an internal audit, assessing the strength of competitors, and choosing a strategy. (moderate, pages 208, 213)

77. **Identify the most common reactive reasons why companies go into international business.**
    To respond to competitors; to get around restrictive trade barriers; to overcome regulations and restrictions by a firm's home government; and to respond to newly emerging customer demands in the international marketplace. (moderate, pages 209-210)

78. **How does Avon adapt its marketing strategy in different markets?**
    Because of the spiraling number of women working outside their homes, Avon had to reengineer its traditional strategy of women making house calls to sell its products. Avon has therefore entered several overseas markets such as Mexico, Poland, China, India, South Africa and Vietnam. In Brazil, Avon saleswomen carry their sample kits to wooden shacks in tiny villages. In China, Avon sets up showrooms in major cities because consumers are suspicious of door to door salespeople. (moderate, pages 210-211)*

79. **What are the most common proactive reasons for which firms enter into international business?**
    To achieve economies of scale; to seek out new expansion opportunities when expansion is limited at home; to rejuvenate mature products or services; to gain greater access to resources and attain cost savings; to take advantage of incentives offered by foreign governments. (moderate, pages 210-211)

80. **Give three primary reasons why strategic planning is more complex on the global level than the domestic level.**
    The three primary reasons are: the difficulty in gaining accurate and timely information; the diversity of geographic locations; and differences in political, legal, cultural, market, and financial processes. (moderate, page 212)

81. **Why is a global orientation to strategic planning important for companies?**
    An ongoing strategic planning process with a global orientation is important because it identifies opportunities for 1) appropriate market expansion, 2) increased profitability, and 3) new ventures by which the firm can exploit its strategic advantages. Even in the absence of immediate opportunities, monitoring the global environment for trends and competition is important for domestic planning. (moderate, page 212)*

82. **List the seven steps in the strategic management process.**
(1) Define the company's mission and objectives; (2) assess the environment for threats and opportunities; (3) assess the company's internal strengths and weaknesses; (4) consider alternative strategies using competitive analysis; (5) choose a strategy; (6) implement the strategy through complementary structure, systems, and operational processes; and (7) set up control and evaluation systems to ensure success and feedback to planning. (difficult, page 213)

83. **Discuss the concept of global environmental analysis.**
The process of gathering information and forecasting relevant trends, competitive actions, and circumstances that will affect operations in geographic areas of potential interest is called environmental scanning. This activity should be conducted on three levels—multinational, regional, and national. (moderate, page 215)

84. **What are the four factors most commonly evaluated in environmental scanning?**
The four factors are: analysis of political instability; analysis of currency instability; analysis of nationalism; and analysis of international competition. (moderate, page 215)

85. **What are the components of scanning at the multinational level?**
Companies should assess the multinational level for significant worldwide trends through identification, monitoring, and forecasting activities. This would include issues in the political, economic, sociocultural, or technological environment. (moderate, page 215)

86. **Compare scanning at the multinational level with regional level scanning.**
Companies should assess the multinational level for significant worldwide trends; at the regional level, the analysis should focus more on the critical environmental factors that would generate threats or opportunities for the company's products, services, or technologies. (moderate, page 215)*

87. **Ideally, companies should conduct global environmental analysis on which different levels?**
Companies should assess the environment at the multinational level, the regional level, and the national level. (easy, page 215)

88. **Why should companies supplement external sources of information with internal ones while performing environmental scanning?**
Many countries, especially developing countries, do not have accurate and reliable data on which companies can base their decisions. Often "official" data is misleading because it is tampered with by government officials for propaganda purposes. Therefore, companies should generate their own internal data sources. (moderate, page 217)*

89. **What does each letter in SWOT stand for? How is it used in strategic planning?**
Each letter stands for strengths, weaknesses, opportunities, and threats. The SWOT analysis is used after assessing the external and internal environments to help firms determine their strategic direction. (easy, page 218)

90. **Which of factors should be considered in assessing a company's strengths and weaknesses? What is a SWOT analysis?**
Corporate strengths and weaknesses are best assessed through an analysis of distinctive competencies (unique capabilities and resources possessed by the firm) and through analysis of core competencies, which represent the collective learning in the organization. A SWOT analysis is a summary of the external issues (opportunities and threats) and internal resources (strengths and weaknesses) that are most likely to influence the future or intended direction of the firm. It helps a firm identify the potential for "fit" between its resources and the environment. (moderate, page 218)*

91. **What do we mean by core competencies, or strategic success factors? Give some examples of these and their role as competitive strategic advantage factors in the planning process.**
Core competencies consist of key strengths that companies build their strategies around. They are internal strengths that can benefit or serve a wide range of products or services. For example, Sony has the capacity to miniaturize and Philips has competency in optical-media expertise. Canon has its core competence in optics and micro-electronics. (moderate, page 218)*

92. **Identify the two levels of strategic alternatives that a firm must consider when competing internationally.**
The first level, global strategic alternatives, determines what overall approach to the global marketplace a firm wishes to take. The second level, entry strategy alternatives, applies to firms of any size; these alternatives determine what specific entry strategy is appropriate for each country in which the firm plans to operate. (moderate, page 219)

93. **Compare and contrast globalization and regionalization.**
Globalization is the strategy of treating the world as one undifferentiated marketplace, and the establishment of worldwide operations and the development of standardized products and marketing. A regionalization strategy focuses more on certain regions of the world only and their distinctiveness. With a regionalization strategy, local markets are linked together within a region allowing more local responsiveness and specialization. Globalization affords economies of scale; regionalization requires flexibility and adaptability. (moderate, pages 219-221)*

94. **When is a regionalization strategy more appropriate than a globalization strategy?**
The regionalization strategy is more effective for those firms that are in multi-domestic industries. In such cases, local markets are linked together within a region, allowing more local responsiveness and specialization. Top managers within each region decide on their own investment locations, product mixes, and competitive positioning- thus running their subsidiaries as quasi-independent organizations. Such a strategy often reduces risk and allows for more adaptation to the local market. (moderate, page 221)*

95. **How does Matsushita follow the strategy "Go Global, Act Local"?**
Matsushita has over 150 production and R&D bases in 38 countries. It tries to localize by employing and training local managers and keeping the expatriate head count down. Other Matsushita local policies are to develop local R&D and to tailor products to markets, to let plants set their own rules, and to be a good corporate citizen in every country that it operates in. (moderate, page 222)*

96. **Identify the ten most common entry strategy alternatives.**
The ten most common entry strategies are: exporting, licensing, franchising, contract manufacturing, offshoring, service sector outsourcing, turnkey operations, management contracts, international joint ventures, and wholly-owned subsidiaries. (moderate, pages 225-230)

97. **What factors should a company consider when it decides to follow a service sector outsourcing strategy in another country?**
While most companies look at the lower wages prevalent in the foreign country, other factors that need to be considered are the tax environments in those countries, the impact on supply chain costs, and the cost of office or plant or office shutdown. (moderate, page 227)*

98. **Identify some examples of location factors that influence the choice of international market entry mode.**
Six factors identified by the text are: extent of scale and location economies, country risk, cultural distance, knowledge of the local market, potential of the local market, and competition in the local market. (moderate, page 235)

99. **Upon which three factors does the choice of an entry strategy depend?**
Entry strategy depends on three main factors: evaluation of the advantages and disadvantages of each alternative strategy relative to the firm's capabilities; analysis of critical environmental factors; and the contribution each alternative would make to the overall mission and objectives of the company. (moderate, page 230)*

Comprehensive Essay Questions

100. **Must a firm be proactive in internationalizing its operations in order to be successful?**
The text does not make this assertion, although it does state that to remain competitive, companies should move fast to build strong positions in world markets (i.e., should be proactive or aggressive). Clearly, the motives for being proactive relate to profitability (economies of scale, new market opportunities, resource access, and cost savings). It appears a firm can be profitable without being proactive. It seems they would be more profitable if they were proactive. (moderate, page 209)*

101. **Exhibit 6-3 identifies a full range of global corporate objectives. In what ways might the functional objectives (marketing, finance, etc.) conflict with each other? How might these conflicts be resolved?**
There are a number of potential conflicts between objectives. For example, the marketing objective "growth in market share" might conflict with a number of profitability goals. The venture could buy market share by lowering its price and therefore its profits, or it could spend excessive amounts on advertising. Similarly in production, the ratio of foreign to domestic production might change the economies of scale at either location and adversely affect profit. To resolve these conflicts, the company needs to agree on its time horizon, e.g., is it interested in market share today or the growth in market share over ten years? Second, it needs to consider the conflict in goals during the planning stage so that it can prioritize its objectives over time. (moderate, page 214)*

102. **What factors or variables should a company consider when scanning the environment?**
Environmental scanning should focus on the future interest of the firm and should cover several major variables:
1) Political stability: a volatile political environment is an uncontrollable risk to the company that may result in loss of not only profitability but also ownership.
2) Currency stability: high fluctuations in exchange rates and high inflation rates affect the profitability of the company
3) Nationalism: host governments may impose restrictive policies- limits on repatriation of profits, local equity requirements, local content requirements, which may hinder smooth operations in foreign countries
4) International competition: an assessment of number and size of the competitors to the company both domestic and foreign is very important to assess the scope of operations in the country.
Other factors such as the availability of adequate infrastructure for transportation and communication should also be considered when scanning the environment for strategic planning. (moderate, page 215)*

103. **What are the two strategies of globalization and regionalization? Explain when each strategy can be used effectively.**

A globalization strategy is based on the premise that the world can be approached as an undifferentiated marketplace and the firm can develop and market standardized products. The rationale is to compete by establishing world wide economies of scale, offshore manufacturing, and international cash flows. Companies such as Sony, Caterpillar and ICI follow globalization strategies.

A regionalization strategy is more effective for those firms that are in multi-domestic industries. In such cases, local markets are linked together within a region, allowing more local responsiveness and specialization. Top managers within each region decide on their own investment locations, product mixes, and competitive positioning- thus running their subsidiaries as quasi-independent organizations. Such a strategy often reduces environmental risk and allows for more adaptation to the local market. Samsung Tesco is an example of a firm that has successfully used the regionalization strategy. (moderate, pages 219, 221)*

104. **List five conditions under which alliance-based entry modes are more suitable.**

The five conditions include: (1) physical, linguistic, and cultural distance between home and host countries is high; (2) the subsidiary would have low operational integration with the rest of the multinational operations; (3) the risk of asymmetric learning by the partner is low; (4) the company is short of capital; and (5) government regulations require local equity participation. (moderate, pages 234, 236)

Chapter 7
Global Alliances and Strategy Implementation

Multiple Choice Questions

1. Which of the following is represents strategies followed by Spanish companies as discussed in the Opening Profile?
    a. Acquisition of companies in other parts of Europe.
    b. They traditionally invested in Latin America.
    c. Their expansion into the U.S. has been traditionally limited to Hispanic markets.
    d. All of the above. (easy, pages 242-243)

2. _____ are partnerships between two or more firms who decide they can better pursue their mutual goals by combining their resources as well as their existing distinctive competitive advantages.
    a. Strategic alliances (easy, page 243)
    b. Export management companies
    c. Company subsidiaries
    d. Turnkey operations

3. Alliances are often called _____ and are transition mechanisms that propel the partners' strategy forward in a turbulent environment faster than would be possible for each company alone.
    a. competitive strategies
    b. cooperative strategies (moderate, page 243)
    c. independent strategies
    d. virtual strategies

4. Which of the following is <u>not</u> one of the primary categories under which alliances typically fall?
    a. joint ventures
    b. equity strategic alliances
    c. nonequity strategic alliances
    d. transmodal strategic alliances (moderate, page 244)

5. Alliances in which two or more partners have different relative ownership shares (equity percentages) in the new venture are called _____.
    a. cultural strategic alliances
    b. equity strategic alliances (moderate, page 244)
    c. non-equity strategic alliances
    d. transmodal strategic alliances

6. When France's Thomson combined with China's TCL to form TCL-Thomson electronics with Thomson owning 33% and TCL owning the remaining 67% of the combined company, _____ was formed.
   a. a non-equity strategic alliance
   b. a manufacturing alliance
   c. a global alliance
   d. an equity strategic alliance (moderate, page 244)*

7. Alliances that are carried out through contract rather than ownership sharing are called _____.
   a. cultural strategic alliances
   b. equity strategic alliances
   c. non-equity strategic alliances (moderate, page 244)
   d. transmodal strategic alliances

8. _____ are working partnerships between companies across national boundaries and increasingly across industries.
   a. Global strategic alliances (moderate, page 244)
   b. National strategic alliances
   c. Domestic strategic alliances
   d. Transitional strategic alliances

9. _____ is a typical reason for forming cross-border alliances.
   a. Avoiding import barriers
   b. Sharing R&D costs
   c. Gain access to specific markets
   d. All of the above (easy, page 244-245)*

10. All of the following are motivations and benefits for forming cross-border alliances except to _____.
    a. gain access to specific markets
    b. gain access to markets where regulations favor foreign companies (difficult, pages 244-245)*
    c. avoid protectionist legislation
    d. reduce political risk

11. Agreements with Japan's NEC give AT&T access to _____.
    a. emerging markets
    b. markets that are currently blocked by tariffs
    c. new semiconductor technologies (difficult, page 246)* {AACSB: Uses of Information Technology}
    d. all of the above

12. AT&T's network of alliances around the world has the objective of _____.
    a. access to new markets
    b. access to new technology
    c. cost reduction
    d. a and b only (moderate, page 246)* {AACSB: Uses of Information Technology}

13. In a study of 153 corporate alliances, researchers found that the choice of "means of governance" depended on concern regarding _____.
    a. control over type of structure used
    b. control over information flows pertaining to technology (difficult, page 246) {AACSB: Uses of Information Technology}
    c. control over markets
    d. control over distribution strategies

14. David Lei noted that the single greatest impediment managers face when seeking to learn or renew sources of competitive advantage is that _____.
    a. great venture partners are hard to find
    b. technologies change very rapidly
    c. partners can become competitors (moderate, page 247)
    d. governments can be fickle

15. Which of the following is a concern that American computer makers have with production in China?
    a. The Chinese market is not large enough to sell their products domestically.
    b. There will be loss of intellectual property if Chinese companies co-produce the computers. (moderate, page 247-248)* {AACSB: Uses of Information Technology}
    c. There are not enough high skilled workers available in China for American companies.
    d. All of the above

16. The dual role of strategic alliance refers to _____.
    a. the need to find resources and markets
    b. the need to find people and processes
    c. the conflict between cooperation and competition (moderate, page 247)
    d. the conflict between home and host governments

17. Which of the following are examples of the cooperative aspect of strategic alliances?
    a. economies of scale in tangible assets
    b. upstream – downstream division of labor
    c. limited investment risk via shared resources
    d. all of the above (moderate, page 248)*

18. Which of the following is an example of the competitive aspect of strategic alliances?
    a. economies of scale in tangible assets
    b. upstream-downstream division of labor
    c. **encircling existing competitors with alliance partners (difficult, page 248)* {AACSB: Uses of Information Technology}**
    d. creating a critical mass to develop new technologies

19. To minimize potential problems in alliances, companies should _____.
    a. be the first foreign company in a market to select a local partner
    b. **choose a partner with complementary products (difficult, page 248-250)**
    c. choose a partner with the largest presence in the target market
    d. choose a partner with the strongest technology

20. Respondents to a survey of 158 investors and non-investors in Russia in 2005 indicated that doing business in Russia was _____.
    a. less risky and more profitable than China, India, and south-east Asia
    b. **more risky and less profitable than China, India, and south-east Asia (moderate, page 249}**
    c. as profitable as doing business in western Europe
    d. as profitable as doing business in the United States and Canada

21. The level of uncertainty of foreign investors in Russia was fueled by the experiences of _____.
    a. Boeing's joint venture with Russian aircraft maker Tupolev
    b. McDonald's in Moscow
    c. **General Motors's joint venture with Russian car maker OAO Avtovaz (easy, page 250)**
    d. All of the above

22. The main concern about doing business in Russia was_____..
    a. corruption
    b. bribe taking
    c. weak legislative and enforcement regimes
    d. **all of the above (easy, page 250) {AACSB: Ethical Reasoning}**

23. Despite the uncertainties, Russia is one of the fastest growing regions for global consumer giants such as _____.
    a. Coca Cola
    b. Procter & Gamble
    c. Nestle
    d. **All of the above (moderate, page 250)**

24. According to Buckley, managers of foreign companies planning to set up business in Russia should consider the following:
    a. Bribe paying may be necessary given the level of corruption.
    b. Assign funds for local promotion and advertising to establish your corporate image (difficult, page 250) {AACSB: Ethical Reasoning}
    c. To control corruption and mismanagement, use American managers for the venture.
    d. All of the above.

25. Hitt et al. found that the less stable Russian institutional environment has influenced Russian managers to _____.
    a. focus more on the short term
    b. select partners that provide access to financial capital
    c. select partners that have complementary capabilities
    d. all of the above (easy, page 250)

26. Which of the following is <u>not</u> a characteristic of strategic implementation of the McDonald's corporation?
    a. minimize autonomy (moderate, page 250)*
    b. hire locals whenever possible
    c. form paradigm-busting arrangements with suppliers
    d. tweak the standard menu only slightly from place to place

27. All of the following are examples of strategic implementation by the McDonald's corporation <u>except</u> _____.
    a. use a market skimming strategy to gain acceptance by innovators (difficult, page 250)*
    b. know a country's culture before entering the market
    c. hire locals whenever possible
    d. maximize autonomy

28. Strategic alliance implementation plans require setting up _____ throughout the organization.
    a. overall policies
    b. administrative responsibilities
    c. organizational schedules
    d. all of the above (moderate, page 250)

29. An overarching factor affecting all other variables necessary for successful implementation is that of _____.
    a. leadership (easy, page, 251)
    b. structure
    c. system
    d. performance

30. International joint venture control is defined as the process through which a parent company ensures that the way a joint venture is managed conforms to _____.
    a. international accounting standards
    b. qualitative standards ahead of quantitative standards
    c. its own interest (moderate, page 252)
    d. quantitative standards ahead of qualitative standards

31. Organizational design as a mechanism of joint venture control refers to _____.
    a. the architectural plans of the joint venture
    b. the functional structure in the joint venture
    c. the geographic structure of the joint venture
    d. the relative amount of decision-making power that the joint venture will have (difficult, page 252)

32. The most important single factor which will determine success or failure in an international joint venture is _____.
    a. the financial help of both partners
    b. compatibility of partner strategies
    c. willingness of the smaller partner to compromise its interests when necessary in the short run
    d. choice of the international joint venture partner (moderate, page 252)

33. Most problems with international joint ventures involve _____.
    a. the parent corporation
    b. the local partner (moderate, page 252)*
    c. differences in accounting standards between nations
    d. differences in control system information management between nations

34. Where ownership is divided among several partners, the parents are more likely to delegate the operational running of the IJV to _____.
    a. the local IJV management (moderate, page 253)
    b. parent company management
    c. middle managers at the parent company level
    d. the management team from the largest company in the joint venture

35. Opening your own subsidiary in the host country may be better than contracting with an outside firm in the host country if it is crucial for you to ____.
    a. produce gains in efficiency, productivity, and quality
    b. keep control of proprietary technology and processes (easy, page 251) {AACSB: Uses of Information Technology}
    c. minimize jobs losses in the home country
    d. market your products in the host country

36. We can conclude from the research studies by Geringer, Schaan, and Beamish that _____.
    a. **parent companies focus their monitoring efforts on a few activities that they consider important (difficult, page 253)***
    b. parent companies exert tremendous efforts on monitoring day-to-day activities of the joint venture
    c. once the joint venture is formed, parent companies leave it alone
    d. as long as the joint venture posts a profit, parent companies are not concerned with how it is generated.

37. Research has identified three control dimensions in international joint ventures: the extent of degree of control, the mechanisms of control, and the _____.
    a. objective of control
    b. **focus of control (moderate, page 253)**
    c. locus of control
    d. culture of control

38. Which of the following is not related to using indirect mechanisms to control an international joint venture?
    a. parent organizational and reporting structure
    b. staffing policies
    c. close coordination with the international joint venture general manager
    d. **all of the above (difficult, page 253)***

39. The extent of control exercised over an IJV by its parent is determined by the decision-making autonomy delegated to IJV management, which is largely dependent upon _____.
    a. **staffing choices (moderate, page 253)***
    b. policies
    c. strategy
    d. structure

40. The extent of control exercised over the IJV by its parent companies seems to be primarily determined by _____.
    a. the financial sophistication of the parent company
    b. **the decision-making autonomy delegated by the parent company to the international joint venture management (moderate, page 253)**
    c. the experience of subsidiary managers
    d. the experience of parent company managers

41. All of the following are examples of international joint venture control mechanisms used by parent firms except _____.
    a. staffing policies
    b. reporting arrangements
    c. **government controls (moderate, page 253)**
    d. close coordination with the IJV general manager

42. Which of the following are knowledge management processes?
   a. transfer of existing knowledge
   b. transformation and creation of knowledge
   c. harvest of knowledge from IJV to parents
   d. all of the above (easy, 254)*

43. The profitability of international joint ventures is greatly influenced by _____ and _____.
   a. local management; product choices
   b. tax level; profit repatriation restrictions (difficult, page 254)*
   c. demographics; culture
   d. all of the above

44. All of the following represent government influences on international joint ventures except _____.
   a. copyright protection
   b. labor union rules
   c. patent protection
   d. negotiation practices (moderate, page 254)

45. In 1993, Caterpillar faced a problem in China because _____.
   a. the government revoked their tax breaks and restricted foreign investment (moderate, page 255)*
   b. the government decided to control currency outflows
   c. the government asked Caterpillar to withdraw from its market in China
   d. the government forced Caterpillar to export its products to other countries

46. One of the key differences between Western expatriates and Hungarian managers is that while _____.
   a. Western expatriates are driven by market-driven technology, Hungarians are driven by volume-driven technology (difficult, page 256)*
   b. Western expatriates have large hierarchical structures, Hungarians have flat structures
   c. Western expatriates have opaque information systems, Hungarians have transparent information systems
   d. Western expatriates have administrative HR systems, Hungarians have strategic HR systems.

47. _____ is one variable that is often overlooked when deciding on entry strategies and alliances, particularly when the target country is perceived to be similar to the home country.
   a. Political stability
   b. Culture (moderate, page 255)*
   c. Currency stability
   d. Competition

48. According to Rosenzweig, which of the following American characteristics causes the most problems for Americans in their relationships with Europeans?.
   a. Americans tend to have a world perspective.
   b. Americans are accepting of having a European boss.
   c. Americans tend to be too formal.
   d. **Americans need autonomy and independence on the job. (moderate, page 256)**

49. Rozensweig quotes a French manager saying, "…Americans are the least international of all people, because _____."
   a. **their home market is so big (moderate, page 256)**
   b. they only speak English
   c. their egos are too big
   d. they've forgotten their heritage

50. What did Mercedes Benz do to adapt to U.S. culture and management styles in its Tuscaloosa, Alabama, plant?
   a. Designed the plan so that any worker could stop the assembly line to correct problems.
   b. Formed workers into teams that met every day to solve problems.
   c. Replaced uniforms with casual shirts with names on the pockets.
   d. **All of the above (easy, page 257)***

51. What cultural tradition did the Mittal merger with Acelor violate?
   a. Europeans resented control by a company in a developing country.
   b. Indian culture required Mittal to fire all European managers.
   c. The European culture was too informal for the Mittal top managers.
   d. **The Marwari believe that it is critical for companies to maintain family ownership (easy, page 257-258)**

Short Essay Questions

52. **What are strategic alliances? Explain their role in globalization.**
   Strategic alliances are partnerships with other companies formed for a number of practical purposes, such as avoiding import barriers and licensing requirements, to share costs of R&D, to gain access to specific markets, to reduce political risks, and to take advantage of synergies. Alliances are playing an increasing role in globalization as companies often form such alliance to enter foreign markets to reduce risks. (moderate, page 244-247)* {AACSB: Global}

53. **Why would a company seek an alliance over some other form of market entry?**

An alliance is usually with a business firm, but it may also be with a foreign government. Alliances have advantages over other entry forms, such as exporting. For example, an alliance will give faster market access than exporting and will avoid entry barriers such as tariffs. In addition, while an exporting strategy requires the firm to find customers, the alliance partner may already have a customer base. Further, an alliance is a means of spreading risk over a larger, more diversified enterprise than a single domestic firm. In large technological firms an alliance is often a way to share costs and share technology. (moderate, page 244-247)*

54. **What motivates a company to develop a cross-border alliance?**

The commonly noted motivations for developing a cross-border alliance include: to avoid import barriers, licensing requirements and other protectionist legislation; to share the costs and risks of the research and development of new products and processes; to gain access to specific markets, such as the EU, where regulations favor domestic companies; market entry into some countries may only be attained through alliances—typically joint ventures; to reduce political risk while making inroads into a new market; to gain rapid entry into a new or consolidating industry; and to take advantage of synergies. Technology is rapidly providing the means for overlapping and merging of traditional industries such as entertainment. (difficult, page 245-247)*

55. **What are some of the challenges in implementing global alliances?**

Problems with shared ownership, differences in national cultures, the integration of widely different structures and systems, the distribution of power between the companies involved, and the conflicts in their relative locus of decision making and control. (easy, page 247)

56. **Describe the criteria a firm should use to keep an alliance from becoming a new form of competition.**

Firms should pick a compatible partner and take time to know the partner through a long "courtship" period. Choose a partner with complementary skills, products, and markets. Work out an agreement on how proprietary technology will be handled – what will be shared, and what will not. Finally, recognize that the alliance will likely be short and as such, you must rapidly learn the partner's technology. (moderate, page 248-249) {AACSB: Use of Information Technology}

57.   **What are some of the areas of incompatibility among partners in cross-border alliances?**
       In addition to potential loss of proprietary technology, other areas of incompatibility often arise, such as conflicting strategic goals and objectives, cultural clashes, and disputes over management and control systems. The alliance between KLM and Northwest Airlines resulted in a bitter feud among top officials of both companies over cultural differences between the companies as well as a power struggle at the top. (moderate, page 254-255)* {**AACSB: Use of Information Technology**}

58.   **What is meant by the "dual nature" of strategic alliances?**
       Alliances serve both a cooperative and a competitive role. Ventures start on the surface as cooperative agreements. There is a dynamic tension under the surface, as venture partners have the potential to become new competitors—competitors with significant knowledge of their partner's operations and strategy. (moderate, page 247) {**AACSB: Use of Information Technology**}

59.   **Why is Russia considered an risky country for joint ventures and what are some of the specific risks?**
       Some foreign companies have been concerned about investing in Russia since President Putin's moves to take control of key industries, including banks, newspapers, and oil assets. For example, he has renationalized the Yukos oil company, the largest oil company in Russia. A survey of 158 corporate investors and non-investors in 2005 indicated that they thought doing business in Russia more risky and less profitable than China, India, and south-east Asia. Some specific risks cited in the study were corruption, bribe-taking by the state bureaucracy, and weak legislative and enforcement mechanisms. (moderate, page 249-250)* {**AACSB: Ethical Reasoning**}

60.   **Are there opportunities in Russia for American companies? If so, what are some examples?**
       Despite the problems, there are opportunities in Russia in consumer products, software, hotels, and heavy industrial production. Moscow and major cities are experiencing a consumer boom as a result of rising incomes. Russia is one of the fastest growing countries for companies such as Coca-Cola, Procter & Gamble, and Nestle. These join other firms such as Caterpillar, IBM, GE, Ford, Hewlett-Packard, Pepsi-Co., Eastman Kodak, and AT&T. Some firms, such as Bell Labs, which need skilled R&D personnel, are finding those personnel in Russia. (moderate, page 250)* {**AACSB: Use of Information Technology**}

61. **What are the goals of potential Russian firms when they seek alliances with foreign companies?**
A study by Hitt et al. found that the less stable Russian institutional environment influenced Russian managers to focus more on the short term. Russian managers also selected partners that could provide access to financial capital and complementary capabilities that would allow the firm to weather the turbulent Russian business environment. (difficult, page 251) {AACSB: Multicultural and Diversity}

62. **What is meant by international joint venture control? Why is it such an important issue?**
International joint venture control is defined as the process through which a parent company ensures that the way a joint venture is managed conforms to its own interest. The most important single factor, which will determine success or failure, is the choice of the IJV partner. IJV control is an important issue because at least one parent is headquartered outside the venture's country of operations thus requiring unique measures of control. Lack of attention to specific control requisites of IJVs can limit the parent company's ability to efficiently utilize its resources, coordinate its activities, and implement its strategy. (moderate, page 253)*

63. **Schaan argues that IJV control is "the process through which a parent company ensures that the way a joint venture is managed conforms to its own interest." What problems do you see with this concept?**
If both partners view control the same way, they will both try to manage the venture to their own interest. Those two interests may be very different. For Schaan's model to work to its best, the parties must agree on the objectives of the venture.   (moderate, page 253)*

64. **What is the single most important factor that will determine the success or failure of IJV control? Why do you feel this is true?**
Most researchers point to the choice of the IJV partner. Of all the decisions made in an IJV, this one would be the most difficult to reverse.
(moderate, page 253)

65. **Why are international joint ventures like a marriage?**
International Joint Ventures are like a marriage because the more issues which can be settled and agreed upon before the merger, the less likely it will be to break up. This agreement should specify the rights and responsibilities of each partner. There is also the issue of compatibility. Incompatible ventures dissolve as do incompatible marriages. To become and remain compatible, venture partners need to appreciate the cultural heritage of their partner.
(moderate, pages 253-254)*

66. **Describe the process of knowledge management in international joint ventures.**
Knowledge management is the conscious and active management of creating, disseminating, evolving and applying knowledge to strategic ends. Exhibit 7-2 graphically describes this process as consisting of several components: 1) transfer: managing the flow of existing knowledge between parents and from parents to IJV, 2) transformation: managing the creation of knowledge and transformation within the IJV, and 3) harvest: managing the flow of the transformed and newly created knowledge back to parent. (moderate, pages 254-255)

67. **How do European managers perceive their American employees?**
European managers appreciate that Americans are pragmatic, open, forthright, and innovative. They also say that the tendency of Americans to be informal and individualistic means that their need for independence and autonomy on the job causes problems in their relationship with head office Europeans. Europeans believe that Americans do not generally like taking orders and directives from foreign-based headquarters. (easy, page 263)*

68. **List some comments that French managers typically make regarding their activities in the United States to portray what they think of Americans..**
(1) "Americans see themselves as the world's leading country, and it's not easy for them to accept having a European in charge;" (2) "It is difficult for Americans to develop a world perspective;" (3) "The horizon of Americans often goes only as far as the U.S. border;" and (4) "It might be said that Americans are the least international of all people, because their home market is so big." (difficult, page 257-258)* {**AACSB: Multicultural and Diversity**}

69. **How did the German trainers adapt to American culture in the Mercedes plant?**
The German trainers recognized that the whole concept of building a Mercedes quality car had to be taught to the American workers in a way that would appeal to them. Instead of organizing according to strict German hierarchy they designed the plant such that any worker could stop the assembly line to correct manufacturing problems. They formed workers into teams that met everyday with the trainers to problem-solve. They replaced formal offices and uniforms with casual personalized shirts. To add to the collegiality, get-togethers for a beer after work became common. The local community responded by having beer fests and including German-language stations on local cable TV. (moderate, page 258)* {**AACSB: Multicultural and Diversity**}

70. **Explain the concepts of guanxi and guanxihu.**
    Guanxi refers to the relationship networks that bind Chinese firms into social and business webs and plays an important role in the success of those firms. Nothing gets done without these direct or indirect connections. *Guanxihu* is a new term which refers to a bond between specially connected firms that generates preferential treatment to members of the network. Even withdrawal is difficult without *guanxi* as experienced by Audi whose joint venture partner appropriated its car design and manufacturing process after Audi decided to terminate its joint venture with its Chinese partner. (moderate, page 259)*

Comprehensive Essay Questions

71. **Discuss Lei's concerns about the dual nature of strategic alliances. Give examples of firms that have been able to appropriate knowledge from alliances and apply that knowledge to other uses.**
    Lei is quoted in the text, "Perhaps the single greatest impediment managers face when seeking to learn or renew sources of competitive advantage is to realize that cooperation can represent another form of unintended competition, particularly to shape and apply new skills to future products and businesses." The dual nature of strategic alliances provides an explanation for why cross-border alliances have difficulty in collaborating. This is especially true in competitively sensitive areas. The result is mistrust and secrecy which then undermines the alliance. Managers may fear that they will lose the competitive advantage of the firm's proprietary technology or the specific skills that their personnel possess. The cumulative learning that a partner attains through the alliance could potentially be applied to other products or even other industries that are beyond the scope of the alliance, and therefore would hold no benefit to the partner holding the original knowledge. As noted by Lei, the Japanese, in fact have far "out-learned" their U.S. allies in developing and applying new technologies to other uses. Examples of foreign firms that have been able to appropriate knowledge from an alliance are in the power-equipment industry (e.g., Westinghouse-Mitsubishi), the office equipment industry (Kodak-Canon), and in the consumer electronics industry (General Electric-Samsung), (RCA, Sony). (difficult, page 248)* {**AACSB: Use of Information Technology**}

72. **Discuss four guidelines that should be followed to increase the likelihood of success for alliances.**
    (1) Choose a partner with compatible strategic goals and objectives and one with whom the alliance will result in synergies through the combined markets, technologies, and management cadre; (2) seek alliances where complementary skills, products, and markets will result; (3) work out with the partner how proprietary technology or competitively sensitive information will be handled; and (4) recognize that most alliances last only a few years and will probably break up once a partner feels that it has incorporated the skills and information it needs to go it alone. Therefore, plan an exit strategy. (moderate, page 255)

Chapter 8
Organization Structure and Control Systems

Multiple Choice Questions

1. Cemex, CNOOC, Embraer, Haier, and Infosys Technologies are all examples of_____.
   a. Chinese companies
   b. EU-based companies
   c. US multinationals
   d. **Emerging market companies (easy, page 265)***

2. Many emerging market companies are avoiding the traditional method of internationalization and instead capitalizing on the _____.
   a. opportunities in China
   b. lowering in trade barriers
   c. **born global phenomenon (moderate, page 265)**
   d. access to cheap labor

3. Currently, a multitude of changes are in place that will force emerging market companies to redefine their _____ and _____ systems.
   a. **family-based governance; rigid control (moderate, page 265)**
   b. multinational structure; control
   c. exporting; investment
   d. buying; selling

4. Structure must fit _____ or it will not work.
   a. the environment
   b. corporate traditions and history
   c. cultural factors
   d. **strategy (moderate, page 266)**

5. Which of the following is a major variable to take into account in organization design?
   a. size
   b. environment
   c. appropriate technology
   d. **all of the above (moderate, page 266)**

6. _____ is the process by which a firm gradually changes in response to the imperatives of international competition, domestic market saturation, and desire for expansion.
   a. Organizing
   b. Strategy
   c. Localizing
   d. Internationalization (moderate, page 266)

7. Organizations usually organize their early stages of international activity through a(n) _____ division.
   a. international (moderate, page 267)*
   b. centralized
   c. decentralized
   d. localized

8. An international division may be organized along what lines?
   a. vertical and horizontal
   b. differentiated and integrated
   c. centralized and decentralized
   d. functional, product, geographic (moderate, page 267)

9. An international division with an integrated global structure can be organized along all of the following lines except _____.
   a. functional lines
   b. product lines
   c. geographic lines
   d. cultural lines (moderate, pages 267-269)

10. Which of the following is a stage in Stopford's stages model?
    a. domestic structure plus export department
    b. domestic structure plus foreign subsidiary
    c. international division
    d. all of the above (moderate, page 266)

11. All of the following are typical ways in which firms organize their international activities except _____.
    a. domestic structure plus export department
    b. domestic structure plus foreign subsidiary
    c. international division
    d. cultural structure (moderate, pages 266)

12. The creation of a(n) _____ facilitates the beginning of a global strategy.
    a. local division
    b. international division (moderate, page 267)*
    c. transnational division
    d. matrix division

13. Within an international division structure, conflict may arise among divisions of the firms because _____.
    a. the structure is not very efficient
    b. the structure creates diseconomies of scale
    c. more resources tend to be provided to the international division (difficult, page 267)*
    d. the division is not sufficiently responsive to local cultural differences

14. The global _____ structure is designed on the basis of discrete skill areas.
    a. product
    b. area
    c. divisional
    d. functional (moderate, page 267)

15. Company XYZ is a small firm with a highly centralized system. It is most likely to use a _____ structure.
    a. global functional (moderate, pages 267-268)*
    b. global product
    c. global geographic
    d. global cultural

16. Which of the following forms of organization is particularly appropriate for product lines using similar technology and for businesses with a narrow spectrum of customers?
    a. global functional structure (moderate, page 268)*
    b. global product structure
    c. global geographic structure
    d. global cultural structure

17. The advantages of the _____ structure are market concentration, innovation, and responsiveness to new opportunities in a particular environment.
    a. global functional
    b. global product (moderate, page 268)
    c. global geographic
    d. global cultural

18. Strategic business units (SBUs) are most often associated with what organizational stage?
    a. matrix
    b. functional
    c. geographic
    d. global product (moderate, page 268)*

19. In a global product division, each strategic business unit (SBU) is responsible for _____ and _____.
   a. working capital; capital structure
   b. production; sales (moderate, page 268)
   c. integrating its product with other company products; market share
   d. risk management; accounting

20. In a global geographic structure, decisions are made _____.
   a. at the local level (easy, page 268)
   b. at the headquarters level
   c. by the product line managers
   d. by headquarters executives only

21. What is the most common form of organizing foreign operations?
   a. global geographic (moderate, page 268)
   b. global
   c. functional
   d. matrix

22. An advantage of a global geographic structure is that _____.
   a. it assures economies of scale in production
   b. local managers are familiar with the cultural environment, government regulations, and business transactions (difficult, page 269)*
   c. it provides consistent policies and procedures worldwide
   d. None of the selections is correct.

23. Marketing oriented companies like Nestle and Unilever are more likely to use a global _____ structure, since products can be adapted to local requirements.
   a. functional
   b. geographic (easy, page 269)*
   c. matrix
   d. cluster

24. Which organizational form is a hybrid structure with overlapping responsibilities?
   a. global
   b. localized
   c. geographic
   d. matrix (easy, page 270)

25. Regardless of the stage of internationalization, a firm's structural choices always involve which two opposing forces?
    a. strategy and operations
    b. **integration and differentiation (easy, page 270)**
    c. globalization and localization
    d. matrix and decentralization

26. The way a firm is organized along the _____ dimension determines how well its strategies will be implemented.
    a. local – global
    b. high-tech – low tech
    c. homogeneous – diversity
    d. **differentiation – integration (moderate, page 270)**

27. A specific strategy that treats the world as one market by using a standardized approach to products and markets is called _____.
    a. **globalization (moderate, page 270)***
    b. transnationalization
    c. differentiation
    d. integration

28. To achieve rationalization, managers choose the manufacturing location for each product based on where the best _____ can be obtained.
    a. cost
    b. quality
    c. technology
    d. **combination of cost, quality, and technology (easy, page 270)**

29. What is the downside of rationalization?
    a. too much emphasis on centralized decision making
    b. over-reliance on decentralized decision making
    c. use of the matrix structure
    d. **lack of differentiation and specialization for local markets (moderate, page 270)***

30. A problem many companies face in the future is that their structurally sophisticated global networks leave them exposed to _____.
    a. **environmental volatility (moderate, page 270)**
    b. overly centralized structure
    c. overly decentralized structure
    d. the disadvantages of matrix structure

31. The bamboo network refers to _____.
    a. Japanese keiretsu
    b. overseas Chinese global network (easy, page 271)*
    c. the Chinese living in China
    d. all of the above

32. The network of alliances of the ethnic Chinese is based on _____; personal connections among families, business friends and political associations.
    a. guanxi (moderate, page 272)*
    b. keiretsu
    c. legal contracts
    d. written agreements

33. The success of Levi Strauss turns on its ability to fashion a global strategy that doesn't _____.
    a. create an organizational bureaucracy
    b. break up or threaten global alliances
    c. create excessive vulnerability to cultural threats
    d. inhibit local initiative (moderate, page 272)*

34. When the ever-expanding transnational linkages of an MNC consist of different companies, subsidiaries, units of the firm, suppliers, or individuals, they result in

    _____.

    a. profit
    b. financial surpluses
    c. matrix structures
    d. relational networks (moderate, page 275)

35. Royal Phillips Electronics' structure would best be described as a(n) _____.
    a. domestic structure plus export department
    b. international division
    c. global functional structure
    d. network structure (difficult, page 275)*

36. The purpose of Procter & Gamble's new Four Pillars organizational structure was to enable it to _____.
    a. become more local and less global
    b. become more global and less local
    c. become completely global
    d. think globally and act locally (moderate, pages 273-274)*

37. The new organizational structure at Intel which allowed customizing a range of chips in a combination suitable for a particular target market is known as_____.
   a. customization
   b. integration
   c. platformisation (moderate, page 275)
   d. specialization

38. All of the following are characteristics of "transnational capability" except _____.
   a. ability to manage across borders
   b. retain local flexibility
   c. achieve global integration
   d. all of the above (difficult, page 277)

39. Transnational structure, such as what ABB has, is less a matter of boxes on an organizational chart and more a matter of _____.
   a. controls
   b. communication (moderate, page 277)*
   c. alliances
   d. changes

40. The logic of the new global web may be that the location of _____ is unimportant.
   a. markets
   b. a firm's headquarters (moderate, page 277-278)
   c. technology
   d. financing

41. Two major variables in choosing the structure and design of an organization are the opportunities and need for _____ and _____.
   a. globalization; localization (difficult, page 278)
   b. localization; nationalization
   c. nationalization; rationalization
   d. rationalization; globalization

42. According to the text, as a company becomes larger, more complex, and more sophisticated in its approach to world markets, it may evolve into a(n) _____.
   a. transnational corporation (moderate, page 278)
   b. domestic corporation
   c. international corporation
   d. global corporation

43. The _____ strategy is to maximize opportunities for both efficiency and local responsiveness by adopting a structure that uses alliances, networks, and horizontal design formats.
    a. **transnational (moderate, page 278)***
    b. domestic
    c. international
    d. global

44. With a globalization strategy, the need for complex integrating mechanisms is _____, while in a multi-domestic strategy, the need is _____.
    a. **high; low (difficult, page 278)**
    b. low; high
    c. high; medium
    d. medium; very high

45. With a transnational strategy, the need for complex integrating mechanisms is _____, while in an international strategy, the need is _____.
    a. very high; very low
    b. very low; high
    c. **very high; medium (difficult, page 279)**
    d. medium; very high

46. With a transnational strategy, the role of organizational culture is _____, while in a multidomestic strategy, the role of organizational culture is _____.
    a. quite important; not important
    b. not important; very important
    c. **very important; not important (difficult, page 279)***
    d. quite important; very important

47. As signs of _____ appear, a company should analyze its organization design.
    a. efficiency
    b. competitiveness
    c. **work ineffectiveness (easy, page 279)**
    d. a bureaucratic structure

48. Which of the following is an indication of the need for change in organization design?
    a. a change in the size of the corporation
    b. a change in key individuals
    c. morale problems
    d. **all of the above (difficult, page 280)***

49. All of the following are signs of international organizational malaise except
    _____.
    a. clashes among divisions, subsidiaries, and individuals
    b. duplication of administrative personnel and services
    c. unclear lines of reporting
    d. greater demands for information systems (difficult, page 280)*

50. Contingency theory proposes that the best organizational structure is that which_____.
    a. brings about operations efficiency
    b. brings about tight control of subsidiaries
    c. provides for balanced control of subsidiaries
    d. allows the firm to carry out its strategic goals (difficult, page 281)

51. Structure should not be allowed to get bogged down in _____.
    a. change
    b. strategy
    c. goals and mission
    d. the organization's administrative heritage (moderate, page 281)

52. According to the author, most likely, the future for MNC structure lies in _____.
    a. a global web of networked companies (easy, page, 281)
    b. a global functional structure
    c. a global product structure
    d. centralized hierarchy

53. Those who design structures must account for the relationships among the three interdependent factors of _____.
    a. structure, human resources, and financing
    b. differentiation, integration, and alliances
    c. strategy, structure, and staffing (moderate, page 281)
    d. localization, internationalization, and market openness

54. The two primary means of direct control are _____.
    a. financial statements and budgets
    b. currency transactions and currency repatriation
    c. structure and staffing procedures (moderate, page 282)
    d. qualitative and quantitative

55. All of the following are control mechanisms in multinational organizational structures except _____.
    a. output control
    b. bureaucratic control
    c. organization control
    d. virtual control (moderate, page 282)

56. To control the quality of its products in Russia, McDonald's had to develop

    _____.
    a. a transnational network
    b. a preferred supplier program
    c. a total quality management initiative
    d. a strategy of vertical integration (moderate, page 282)*

57. Which of the following is <u>not</u> recognized as a financial variable in MNC reports that complicates financial statements and performance evaluations?
    a. exchange rates
    b. inflation levels
    c. transfer prices
    d. political systems (moderate, page 283)

58. To reconcile accounting statements, MNCs usually require _____ different sets of financial statements from subsidiaries.
    a. three (easy, page 283)
    b. four
    c. five
    d. six

59. Which of the following is a variable that is likely to affect the appropriateness of monitoring systems?
    a. management practices
    b. expectations regarding time and authority
    c. local constraints
    d. all of the above (easy, page 283)

60. Ueno and Sekaran say their research shows that U.S. companies, compared to Japanese companies, _____.
    a. use long-term evaluations to a greater extent
    b. build budget slack to a lesser extent
    c. use communication more extensively (difficult, page 284)*
    d. all of the above

61. Research by Neghandi and Welge on types of functional reports required from subsidiaries by headquarters revealed that _____.
    a. U.S. MNCs submit double the number of reports than do German and Japanese MNCs
    b. German MNCs submit fewer reports than do Japanese MNCs
    c. Japanese MNCs put less emphasis on personnel performance reviews than US and German MNCs
    d. all of the above (difficult, page 284)*

62. _____ would make it difficult to compare the performance of subsidiaries in different countries.
   a. Inflation
   b. Prices of raw materials
   c. Political upheaval
   d. All of the above (easy, page 285)

63. Non-financial measures of performance evaluation of subsidiaries are _____.
   a. productivity measures
   b. market share measures
   c. public image measures
   d. all of the above (easy, page 285)*

Short Essay Questions

64. **What are the major variables, which must be considered in designing a firm's structure?**
   The major variables are strategy, size, appropriate technology, and the external environment. In addition, geographical dispersion, and differences in time, language, cultural attitudes, and business practices affect a firm's structure. (easy, page 266)

65. **Must every firm follow the structural evolution proposed by Stopford?**
   No, Stopford's model is based on what firms have done, not what they will do. Some firms may be able to learn through the experience of others and accelerate their learning curve. Therefore many firms do not follow the various stages in the model and may directly enter into a joint venture or open a subsidiary abroad without ever having exported to that country before.
   (moderate, page 266)*

66. **Explain the use of the international division structure and the different ways in which that division may be organized.**
   The international division structure consists of separating foreign activities from home activities. The firm may organize internationally along functional, product, or geographic, network or relational lines. With this structure, the foreign subsidiaries are organized under the international division, and the subsidiary managers report to the head of the international division. (moderate, page 267)

67. **Discuss the advantages of the global product structure.**
   The advantages of this organizational form are market concentration, innovation, and responsiveness to new opportunities in a particular environment. (moderate, page 268)*

68. **Discuss the characteristics of the global geographic structure.**

In the global geographic structure, divisions are created to cover geographic regions. Each regional manager is then responsible for the operations and performance of the countries in a given region. As a result, country and regional need take precedence over product expertise.(moderate, pages 268-269)*

69. **What are the two essential interrelated tasks of organizing?**

The two essential tasks are differentiation and integration. Differentiation refers to focusing on and specializing in specific markets. In contrast, integration refers to coordinating those differentiated markets. Both differentiation and integration are essential for implementing the firm's strategy. (moderate, page 270)*

70. **Explain "globalization" and the organizational forms that are needed to achieve it.**

Globalization is a strategy which treats the world as one market by employing a standardized approach to products and markets. To achieve globalization, managers choose manufacturing location based on cost, quality, and technology benefits of those locations. Because this typically involves production in different countries and standardization of design and marketing, activities must be coordinated through central headquarters control. (moderate, page 270)

71. **Who are the overseas Chinese and what is their significance to the discussion of international organizational structure?**

The overseas Chinese are the 55 million expatriates from mainland China that operate or manage business around the globe, particularly in Asia (mostly in Taiwan, Indonesia, and Thailand). The overseas Chinese form a Chinese Commonwealth which is a global network of entrepreneurial relationships. It is estimated that the overseas Chinese control $2 trillion liquid assets and contribute about 80% of the capital for the People's Republic of China. (moderate, page 271)*

72. **Compare and contrast the characteristics of the traditional overseas Chinese to the more recent overseas Chinese?**

The traditional overseas Chinese were refugees who fled from China's poverty, disorder, and communism. For these refugees, business became an opportunity for success and the uncertainties and hardships in their new countries led to a way of doing business that was largely confined to family and trusted friends. This business approach led to many self-made billionaires such as Y.C. Wang. More recently, there has been a new wave of overseas Chinese from countries such as Singapore and Indonesia who are attracted by the rapid growth in China. (moderate, pages 271-272)

73. **What are the underlying values that have shaped the distinctive business culture of the overseas Chinese?**

These values include thrift and a very high savings level, extremely hard work, trust in family, adherence to patriarchal authority, investment based on kinship and affiliations, a preference in investment in tangible goods, and a wary outlook on life. (difficult, page 272)*

74. **Explain the need for an MNC to "be global and act local." How can a firm design the organization to enable this?**

In their rush to get on the globalization bandwagon, many firms have sacrificed their ability to respond to local markets and customs. These firms now realize that a compromise must be made along the globalization-regionalization continuum, and they are experimenting with structural forms to help them "be global and act local." For example, Colgate Palmolive has a geographic structure that is responsible for responding to local or regional needs. The heads of these geographic units, however, reports to the CEO who oversees the centralized coordination for technology, finance, and other functions. The transnational organizational form is another type of structure that facilitates local flexibility while achieving global integration. (difficult, pages 270, 272, 276-277)

75. **What is a transnational organization?**

A transnational organization has the ability to manage across national boundaries, retaining local flexibility while achieving global integration. This ability involves linking foreign operations to each other and to headquarters in a flexible way so as to leverage local and central capabilities. (moderate, page 276-277)

76. **List at least five indications of the need for change in organization design.**

(1) A change in the size of the corporation, (2) a change in key individuals, (3) a failure to meet goals, (4) an inability to get things done on time, (5) a consistently overworked top management, (6) a belief that costs are extravagant, (7) morale problems, (8) lengthy hierarchies that inhibit the exercise of strategic control, (9) planning that has become increasingly staff-driven, and (10) innovation that is stifled by too much administration and monitoring of details. (difficult, page 280)

77. **What determines which decisions in the organization are centralized, and which are decentralized?**

In general, centralized decisions are common for certain functions (e.g., finance, research and development) that are organized for the entire organization, whereas other functions (e.g., production, marketing, and sales) are decentralized because decisions in these areas are best made at the subsidiary level. The centralization-decentralization decision is determined primarily by the speed with which decisions have to be made and whether they primarily affect the whole company or a particular subsidiary. (difficult, page 280)*

78. **What are indirect coordinating mechanisms?**
Indirect coordinating mechanisms include sales quotas, budgets, and other financial controls, and feedback reports giving information about the sales and financial performance of the subsidiary for a given period of time. (moderate, page 283)*

79. **Discuss the problems inherent in financial statement reporting by subsidiaries and analysis of those reports at the MNC level.**
Since different accounting principles and standards are used in different national settings, adjustments must be made to statements before they are analyzed by the parent company. An MNC often require three sets of financial statements from subsidiaries. The first set must meet the accounting standards and procedures of the host country. The second set must meet the accounting principles and standards of the home country. The third set of statements translates the second set of statements into the currency of the home country for consolidation purposes. A foreign subsidiary's financial statement must be consolidated line-by-line with those of the parent company. (difficult, page 283)*

80. **According to Egelhoff's research, how does the method of indirect control differ between U.S. and European firms?**
U.S. MNCs monitor subsidiary outputs and rely more frequently upon reported data than do European MNCs. The latter tend to assign more parent company nationals to key positions in foreign subsidiaries and count on a higher level of behavior control than their U.S. counterparts. As a result, American companies can easily compare performance among subsidiaries. In contrast, the European system measures more qualitative aspects of a subsidiary. This method allows a focus on the unique situation of the subsidiary but makes it difficult to compare its performance to other subsidiaries. (moderate, page 283)

81. **Why is it difficult for headquarters managers to evaluate and compare performance across subsidiaries? What are recommendations for overcoming these difficulties?**
Many variables make the comparison among subsidiaries complicated. For example, one country may experience significant inflation, another may experience large currency fluctuations, still another may have problems with local governmental actions. These variables are beyond the control of the subsidiary manager and affect the profitability of the firm. It is therefore recommended that managers adjust the financial statements to reflect the uncontrollable variables peculiar to each country where a subsidiary is located. Another recommendation is to use nonfinancial measures such as market share, productivity, public image, and community involvement. (moderate, page 285)*

Comprehensive Essay Questions

82. **List and discuss the characteristics of the four ways in which an integrated global structure can be organized?**

The integrated global structure can be organized along function, product, geographic, or matrix lines. The global functional structure is designed on the basis of the company functions. Foreign operations are integrated into the activities and responsibilities of each department to gain functional specialization and economies of scale. This form of organization is primarily used by small firms with highly centralized systems. For firms with diversified product lines that have different technological bases and that are aimed at dissimilar or dispersed markets, a global product structure may be more strategically advantageous than a functional structure. The advantages of this organizational form are market concentration, innovation, and responsiveness to new opportunities in a particular environment. In the global geographic structure, divisions are created to cover geographic regions. Each regional manager is then responsible for the operations and performance of the countries within a given region. A matrix structure is a hybrid organization of overlapping responsibilities and is used by some firms, but has generally fallen into disfavor recently. (difficult, page 267-270)*

83. **Do you think it is possible for organization structure to get too complicated and involved? How would you know when this occurs?**

There seems to be a contingency relationship between strategy and structure. A structure may become too complicated and involved if it does not match the strategy. Exhibit 8-8 identifies 11 symptoms indicating when change is needed, including: failure to meet goals, a drop in morale, and an inability to get things done on time. A company with too complex a structure may also show symptoms of organizational malaise, such as, underutilization of overseas assets, duplication of functions and offices, and breakdowns in communication. (moderate, page 279-280)*

Chapter 9
Staffing and Training for Global Operations

Multiple Choice Questions

1. Which of the following is not one of the tenets of the Toyota Way?
   a. Top management only has the authority to stop factory assembly lines. (easy, page, 340)*
   b. Mutual ownership of problems.
   c. Solving problems at the source instead of behind desks.
   d. Constant drive to improve.

2. How does Toyota prepare its executives to enter the leadership at the company?
   a. **It sends them to the Toyota Institute (moderate, page, 340)***
   b. It rotates them through several international assignments.
   c. They must spend three years as apprentices at the Toyota headquarters.
   d. All of the above.

3. _____ is the only source of sustainable competitive advantage available to U.S. companies.
   a. Sourcing of cheap raw materials
   b. The caliber of its people (moderate, page 342)*
   c. Information technology
   d. Capital

4. Ideally, the _____ should dictate the organizational structure and staffing needed by a firm.
   a. clients served
   b. size of the firm
   c. strategy of the firm (moderate, page 342)
   d. management philosophy of the firm

5. Fred has been sent from USA (headquarters) to Tokyo to manage his firm's Japanese subsidiary. This is an example of the _____ staffing approach.
   a. polycentric
   b. regiocentric
   c. global
   d. ethnocentric (moderate, page 343)*

6. When a company suffers from an inadequate number of skilled managers from the local area in which it operates, and close communication is needed between branches and headquarters, which staffing approach is particularly appropriate?
   a. polycentric
   b. regiocentric
   c. global
   d. ethnocentric (moderate, page 343)*

7. Which staffing approach is preferred when an organization has been structured around a centralized approach to globalization?
   a. polycentric
   b. regiocentric
   c. global
   d. ethnocentric (moderate, page 343)

8. _____ are usually preferable where a high level of technical capability is required.
   a. Parent-country nationals (moderate, page 343)
   b. Host-country nationals
   c. Third-country nationals
   d. Cross-country nationals

9. _____ are chosen for new international ventures requiring managerial experience in the parent company and where there is a concern for loyalty to the company rather than to the host country.
   a. Parent-country nationals (moderate, page 343)*
   b. Host-country nationals
   c. Third-country nationals
   d. Cross-country nationals

10. Which of the following is a disadvantage of an ethnocentric staffing approach?
    a. lack of opportunities for advancement for local staff
    b. poor adaptation and effectiveness of expatriates in foreign countries
    c. lack of access to worldwide pool of managerial talent
    d. all of the above (easy, page 343)

11. Local managers are hired to fill key positions in their own company under the _____ staffing approach.
    a. global
    b. polycentric (easy, page 343)*
    c. ethnocentric
    d. regiocentric

12. Which of the following international staffing approaches is more likely to be effective when implementing a multinational strategy?
   a. ethnocentric
   b. polycentric (moderate, page 343)
   c. subcentric
   d. global

13. Which staffing approach will most likely be effective when implementing a global strategy of "acting local"?
   a. polycentric (moderate, page 343)*
   b. regiocentric
   c. ethnocentric
   d. global

14. One advantage of the polycentric staffing approach is _____.
   a. headquarters managers will gain overseas experience
   b. there will be easy coordination between subsidiary and parent company
   c. managers will be familiar with local customs and language (easy, page 343)
   d. there is potential for conflicting loyalties for the local manager

15. When it is important to satisfy a country's legal requirement that a specific proportion of the firm's top managers be citizens of that particular country, which staffing approach has the highest potential?
   a. ethnocentric
   b. global
   c. regiocentric
   d. polycentric (moderate, page 343)*

16. In the _____ staffing approach, the best managers are recruited from within or outside of the company, regardless of nationality.
   a. regiocentric
   b. global (moderate, page 344)
   c. ethnocentric
   d. polycentric

17. Which of the following staffing approaches has the broadest geographical pool from which to recruit?
   a. regiocentric
   b. global (moderate, page 344)
   c. ethnocentric
   d. polycentric

18. Which staffing approach in time results in further development of a global executive cadre?
   a. regiocentric
   b. global (moderate, page 344)
   c. ethnocentric
   d. polycentric

19. As globalization increases, terms such as _____, _____, and _____ are becoming less common.
   a. ethnocentric, polycentric, regiocentric
   b. TCNs, HCNs, expatriates (moderate, page 344)
   c. global, multidomestic, regional
   d. executive, manager, subordinate

20. The term _____ is increasingly replacing the term_____.
   a. global, multidomestic
   b. ethnocentric, polycentric
   c. transpatriate, expatriate (easy, page 344)
   d. world manager, expatriate

21. Recruiting managers from Latin America for a position in Chile is an example of which staffing approach?
   a. global
   b. ethnocentric
   c. regiocentric (moderate, page 344)*
   d. polycentric

22. Which of the following international staffing approaches can produce a specific mix of PCNs, HCNs, and TCNs?
   a. ethnocentric
   b. polycentric
   c. subcentric
   d. regiocentric (moderate, page 344)

23. _____ are also called expatriates.
   a. Parent-country nationals (easy, page 344)
   b. Host-country nationals
   c. Third-country nationals
   d. Cross-country nationals

24. The _____ staffing approach usually results in a higher level of authority and decision making in headquarters compared to the _____ approach.
   a. ethnocentric; polycentric (moderate, page 345)
   b. polycentric; ethnocentric
   c. geocentric; ethnocentric
   d. regiocentric; polycentric

25. According to Kopp, Japanese firms _____.
   a. scored lower than American and European firms in preparing local nationals for advancement (moderate, page 345)*
   b. lack home country personnel who want to work abroad
   c. face expatriate re-entry difficulties
   d. attract high-caliber local nationals to work for the firm

26. Most MNCs start their operations in a particular region using a(n) _____staffing approach and then move to a _____staffing approach.
   a. polycentric; ethnocentric
   b. regiocentric; polycentric
   c. regiocentric; ethnocentric
   d. ethnocentric; polycentric or regiocentric (difficult, page 347)

27. Personnel directors typically select potential expatriates on the basis of _____.
   a. their ability to speak more than one language
   b. their ability to adapt to different cultures
   c. their desire to learn another culture
   d. their domestic track record and technical expertise (difficult, page 347)

28. Which of the following is not a category of success for expatriate managers?
   a. job factors
   b. country factors (difficult, pages 347-348)*
   c. cultural empathy
   d. family situation

29. The expatriate success factors are based on studies of _____ expatriates.
   a. American (moderate, page 348)*
   b. Japanese
   c. German
   d. Italian

30. Most MNCs, with time, move to a polycentric or regiocentric staffing approach because _____.
   a. local governments put pressure to hire local nationals
   b. there is greater cost to hiring expatriates
   c. local managers have increased their level of managerial and technical competence
   d. all of the above (easy, page 347)

31. Concerns about _____ are a source of a debate about staffing policies among human resource management professionals.
    a. whether or not expatriate managers work as well as native managers
    b. whether or not native managers are more capable than expatriate managers
    c. the best way to staff internationally
    d. the need to maintain strategic control over subsidiaries while developing managers with a global perspective (difficult, page 347)*

32. At Matsushita, selection criteria for staffing seem to be similar to those of _____ companies.
    a. Western (moderate, page 347)
    b. European
    c. Latin American
    d. Asian

33. According to research, _____ has been the most frequently cited reason for the failure of expatriate managers who work in foreign subsidiaries of U.S. or European companies.
    a. inability of the spouse to adjust (moderate, page 349)*
    b. lack of training at the beginning of the process
    c. lack of training during the repatriation part of the process
    d. cultural incompatibility

34. According to research by Tung, most U.S. firms failed to include _____ in their assessment of candidates for potential international experience.
    a. ability to learn languages quickly
    b. ability to adapt to other cultures quickly
    c. human relational skills (moderate, page 349)*
    d. previous experience living in different cultures

35. All of the following are major causes of expatriate failure except _____.
    a. selection based on headquarters' criteria
    b. inadequate training
    c. lack of headquarters support
    d. host government intervention (moderate, pages 349-350)

36. Which of the following is not one of the common factors frequently mentioned in research as a major cause of expatriate failure?
    a. insufficient compensation and financial support
    b. lack of support or alienation from headquarters
    c. selection based on assignment needs in host country (difficult, pages 349-350)*
    d. inability to adapt to local culture

37. The direct cost alone of a failed expatriate assignment is estimated to be _____.
   a. $50,000-$75,000
   b. $100,000-$150,000
   c. $200,000-$1.2 million (moderate, page 350)
   d. $1.5-$3.0 million

38. Expatriates from which nation seem to have the highest probability of success in their overseas assignment?
   a. Sweden
   b. Great Britain
   c. Italy
   d. Japan (moderate, page 351)*

39. Which of the following are reasons for success of Japanese expatriates?
   a. Japanese executives are generally posted for a longer time, thus allowing them more time to adjust.
   b. Japanese companies provide better training and support from headquarters.
   c. Japanese executives are not usually accompanied by their families.
   d. all of the above (easy, page, 351)*

40. Which of the following are areas critical to expatriate preparation for an international assignment?
   a. cultural training
   b. language instruction
   c. familiarity with everyday matters
   d. all of the above (moderate, page 351)

41. A state of disorientation and anxiety about not knowing how to behave in an unfamiliar culture is called _____.
   a. culture shock (moderate, page 352)
   b. assimilation
   c. cultural contingency
   d. integration

42. Which of the following are examples of the irritation and hostility stage of culture shock?
   a. homesickness
   b. disorientation
   c. lashing out
   d. all of the above (moderate, page 353)

43. When the expatriate manager and his or her family are able to function effectively in two cultures, it is known as _____.
    a. gradual adjustment
    b. the honeymoon stage
    c. biculturalism (moderate, page 353)*
    d. irritation and hostility

44. Subculture shock is _____.
    a. experienced when a manager is transferred from one part of the country to another dissimilar part (moderate, page 353)
    b. the opposite of culture shock
    c. very different from culture shock
    d. all of the above

45. _____ occurs when a manager is transferred to another part of a country where there are significant cultural differences.
    a. Subculture shock (easy, page 353)
    b. Culture shock
    c. Acculturation shock
    d. Repatriation shock

46. Which of the following is/are (a) training technique(s) classified by Tung?
    a. sensitivity training
    b. cultural assimilator
    c. field experiences
    d. all of the above (moderate, page 353)*

47. Some MNCs are beginning to recognize that there is no substitute for _____ training in early stages of the careers of managers they hope to develop into senior level global managers.
    a. on-the-job training (moderate, page 353)*
    b. role playing
    c. language
    d. cultural assimilation

48. Premature return of expatriates or the unwillingness of managers to take overseas assignments is often due to _____.
    a. the assignment being detrimental to them financially and to their career progression (moderate, page 356)
    b. their being homesick
    c. the company recalling them
    d. all of the above

49. Move a $100,000 expatriate American executive to London, and suddenly he or she costs the employer _____.
    a. $200,000
    b. $300,000 (moderate, page 357)
    c. $400,000
    d. $500,000

50. "Keeping the expatriate whole", in terms of compensation means _____.
    a. ensuring her family goes with her on the overseas assignment
    b. making sure he is compensated to maintain a standard of living equal to his colleagues at home plus paying additional costs (easy, page 357)
    c. making sure she gets paid in the local currency
    d. all of the above

51. To ensure that expatriates do not lose out through their overseas assignment, the _____ approach is often used to equalize the standard of living between the host country and the home country and to add some compensation for inconvenience or qualitative loss.
    a. income statement
    b. balance sheet (moderate, page 357)
    c. cafeteria
    d. revenue generation

52. Which of the following are components of the expatriates total compensation package?
    a. salary
    b. tax equalization
    c. allowances and benefits
    d. all of the above (easy, pages 357-358)

53. It has been a challenge for Starbucks in China to recruit good local managers because_____.
    a. many local managers prefer to work for Chinese rather than American firms
    b. many local managers are not interested in working for Western firms
    c. Starbucks has a bad reputation in China
    d. the demand for local managers by foreign companies exceeds the supply (moderate, page 359)*

54. Chinese recruits at Starbucks have stated that_____.
    a. they want to leave China and live in the United States
    b. they are looking for training opportunities and to advance in a global company (moderate, page 359)*
    c. money is their primary reason for wanting to work for Starbucks
    d. there are not many opportunities at other foreign companies

55. Starbucks in China has found that it can motivate managers in Beijing by _____.
   a. giving them an opportunity to learn
   b. giving them a good working environment
   c. giving them an opportunity to exercise initiative and authority
   d. all of the above (easy, page 360)*

56. Which of the following are examples of changes in HRM policies in Japanese companies?
   a. less emphasis on lifetime employment
   b. making people responsible for their own retirement fund decisions
   c. basing pay on performance rather than seniority
   d. all of the above (moderate, page, 361)*

57. In a study of "The Best International Human Resource Management Practices Project," it was found that Anglo countries believed _____ to be the most important selection criteria.
   a. education level, job interview, and international experience
   b. seniority, technical skills, and interpersonal skills
   c. employment test, work experience, and education level
   d. **job interview, technical skills, and work experience (difficult, page, 362)***

58. In a study of "The Best International Human Resource Management Practices Project," a major selection tool in Korea was _____ whereas in Taiwan, the major selection tool was _____.
   a. employment test; the job interview (difficult, page 362)*
   b. technical skill; work experience
   c. work experience; seniority
   d. job interview, seniority

Short Essay Questions

59. **Explain the "Toyota Way?"**
   The Toyota Way is a set of guidelines for doing things that permeates the organization. The specific guidelines are mutual ownership of problems, solving problems at the source instead of behind desks, and a constant drive to improve. (moderate, page 340)*

60. **How does Toyota prepare it executives for leadership and instill them with the Toyota values?**
   The Toyota Institute is charged with preparing executives by inculcating them with Toyota's management secrets and culture. The institute is Toyota's best effort to keep the company focused on its original mission of winning customers with quality cars. The institute sends its executives to offices around the world as missionaries for the Toyota Way. (moderate, page 341)*

61. **Why has Toyota been having recent problems disseminating the Toyota Way?**
Toyota is growing more quickly than its ability to transplant its culture to foreign markets. Today, only a third of its total workers are employed at 18 plants in Japan, and much of its global empire does not always march to the same tune. (moderate, page 341)*

62. **How did Toyota adapt its culture to fit the American culture?**
Toyota dropped the requirement for group calisthenics at its American factories. (easy, page 341)* {AACSB: Multicultural and Diversity}

63. **List two disadvantages of using the ethnocentric staffing approach.** Two disadvantages of the ethnocentric approach are (1) lack of opportunities or development for local managers, thereby decreasing their morale and their loyalty to the subsidiary, and (2) the poor adaptation and lack of effectiveness of expatriates in foreign countries. (moderate, page 343)*

64. **Briefly define ethnocentric, polycentric, regiocentric, and global staffing.**
Ethnocentric staffing fills key managerial positions with people from headquarters; polycentric hires to fill key positions with people in their own country; regiocentric hires from a given larger region; and global staffing approach refers to recruiting staff from anywhere in the world. (moderate, pages 343-344)*

65. **Define and explain PCNs, HCNs, and TCNs.**
Parent country nationals (managers from the headquarters); host country managers (managers from the country in which the subsidiary is located); and third country nationals (managers from any country other than the headquarters or the county in which the subsidiary is located). (easy, pages 343-344)

66. **Identify two advantages of using the global staffing approach.**
The advantages include (1) a greater pool of qualified and willing applicants from which to choose, and (2) where third-county nationals are used, more cultural flexibility and adaptability, as well as better bilingual and multilingual skills than PCNs. (moderate, page 344)*

67. **List the five categories of success for expatriate managers.**
The five categories are job factors, relational dimensions such as cultural empathy and flexibility, motivational state, family situation, and language skills. (moderate, pages 347-348)

68. **Identify any five of the seven most common causes of expatriate failure.**
Selection based on headquarters criteria rather than assignment needs; inadequate preparation and training; alienation from headquarters; inability to adapt to local culture; problems with spouse or family; insufficient compensation; and poor programs for career support and repatriation. (moderate, pages 348-349)

69. **Explain the difference between culture shock and subculture shock.**
Culture shock occurs when the individual first begins working in a new culture. Subculture shock occurs when a manager is transferred to another part of the country where there are cultural differences between majority and minority cultures. For example, someone moving from New York to Texas will experience significant differences in cultures between the two states. (moderate, pages 352-353)*

70. **According to Oberg, what are the four stages of culture shock?**
The four stages are: honeymoon stage, irritation and hostility, gradual adjustment, and biculturalism. (moderate, page 353)

71. **Briefly explain any four of the five training technique classifications identified by Tung.**
Area studies (documentary programs about the country's geography, economics, and other areas); culture assimilators (exposure of trainees to the kinds of situations they will experience in the assignment); language training, sensitivity training, and field experiences (exposure to people of other cultures within the trainee's country). (moderate, page 353)

72. **What are some of the variables to consider when compensating host country nationals?**
Some of the variables to be taken into account while compensating host country nationals are local market factors and pay scales, cost of living, government specified benefits, and the role of unions. For example, in Eastern Europe people spend 35-40% of their disposable income on food and utilities thus requiring a large portion of compensation in cash (as opposed to long-term incentives, benefits, and perks which are common in the United States). In Eastern Europe, then, the MNC must focus on providing HCNs with goods and services that are either not available at all or very expensive in that region. (moderate, page 361)*

Comprehensive Essay Questions

73. **Tung has identified five training techniques to assist expatriate employees in the adjustment process. You wish to maximize the results of your expatriate employees. Do you need to use all five techniques?**
It may be that some employees already possess certain knowledge and skill sets that would make them effective interculturally. It would be appropriate to screen expatriate candidates to see what specific training they might need. To truly maximize results, a manager would not want to minimize the importance of training. The text is very clear that the failure rate of U.S. expatriates is high and the expenses associated with failure are significant. Companies need to consider training an investment that has clear returns. The intensity of the training and the methods used will depend on the type of assignment, the country of assignment and the level of preparedness of the manager being posted. If the employee has completed the techniques, additional field experiences might be included such as the placement of the expatriate family with a host family as part of an immersion and familiarization program. (moderate, page 353)*

74. **How does Starbucks recruit, train and retain its managers in China?**
Starbucks can attract young Chinese talent because of its good reputation. Chinese recruits are attracted to companies that train them, and give them an opportunity for advancement, rather than just money alone. These recruits know that managers with experience in Western firms can more easily get jobs. The Starbucks training program begins with bringing new Chinese recruits to Tacoma in Washington. Here, they get a taste of the West Coast lifestyle and the company's informal culture such as Western style barbeques. They are then trained in making cappucinos and dozens of fancy coffees in the stores. By providing a casual atmosphere, a learning environment and trust in their employees, Starbucks can retain its young employees in China. (moderate, pages 359-360)*

75. **With reference to the "Best Human Resources Management Practices Project," discuss the four practices that researchers found to be universal within the cultures studied. Then, give an example of a practice that differed across two countries.**
The researchers found four practices that were universal across the countries studied: 1) pay incentives should not comprise too much of an employee's package; 2) compensation should be based on individual job performance; 3) a reduction in emphasis on seniority; and 4) benefits should comprise an important part of a compensation package. An example of a practice that differed across two countries was that of selection. In Korea, the employment test was the major selection tool, whereas in Taiwan, it was the job interview. (difficult, page 362)*

Chapter 10
Developing a Global Management Cadre

Multiple Choice Questions

1. What did Philip Shearer (Clinique) learn from living in different countries?
    a. humility and the notion that nothing is easy for everyone
    b. people will trust you if you are trustworthy and credible
    c. wherever you are, you have to deliver
    d. all of the above (easy, pages 368-369)*

2. Which of the following are components of developing an international cadre?
    a. preparation
    b. adaptation
    c. repatriation
    d. **all of the above (easy, page 370)**

3. Many companies do little to minimize the potential effects of _____ .
    a. overseas assignments
    b. culture shock
    c. reverse culture shock (moderate, page 370)
    d. projected cognitive similarity

4. Reverse culture shock occurs primarily because of the difficulty of _____ .
    a. reintegration into the home society
    b. reintegration with friends and family members
    c. **reintegration into the organization (moderate, page 370)**
    d. lack of formal training within the organization

5. _____ occurs because the longer a person is away the more difficult it is to get back into the swing of things.
    a. Reverse culture shock (moderate, page 370)
    b. Culture shock
    c. Virtual culture shock
    d. Assimilation

6. A survey by the American Society of Personnel Administration International (ASPAI) revealed that only_____of companies had formal repatriation programs for executives.
    a. 5%
    b. 12%
    c. 31% (moderate, page 370)
    d. 75%

7. Which of the following is correct about repatriation?
   a. Few good managers will take international assignments if they see those assignments resulting in lost promotions at home.
   b. In many U.S. multinationals, employees commonly see overseas assignments as negative career moves.
   c. In many European, Japanese, and Australian companies, overseas assignments are viewed positively.
   d. **All of the above (moderate, page 370)***

8. Successful repatriation is important to the parent company because _____.
   a. they have spent so much developing each expatriate
   b. it signals to the other members that expatriates can be successful
   c. it improves the ability to recruit new expatriate managers
   d. **all of the above (difficult, page 370)***

9. All of the following are examples of support systems recommended by Tung for a successful repatriation program except _____.
   a. mentor program
   b. special career planning unit
   c. system to supply information to expatriates
   d. **repatriation compensation program (difficult, page 371)***

10. As women continue to move up the corporate ladder, the accompanying (trailing) spouse is often male – estimated at _____ in the year 2000.
    a. 5%
    b. 15%
    c. **25% (moderate, page 371)**
    d. 50%

11. Research on 321 American expatriate spouses shows that effective cross-cultural adjustment by spouses is more likely when _____.
    a. firms seek the spouse's opinion about the assignment
    b. the spouse initiates his or her own predeparture training
    c. firms seek the spouse's opinion on the expected standard of living
    d. **all of the above (difficult, page 371)**

12. All of the following are stages in the expatriate transition process except _____.
    a. home country exit transition
    b. **compensation adjustment (easy, page 372)**
    c. host country entry transition
    d. entry transition back to the home country

13. Which of the following is a phase of the transition process experienced by the company's international management cadre over time?
    a. exit transition from home country
    b. entry transition to host country
    c. entry transition back to home country
    d. all of the above (easy, page 372)*

14. _____ and _____ are examples of the home country exit transition.
    a. Host culture sensitivity training; predeparture training (difficult, page 372)
    b. Compensation adjustment; predeparture training
    c. Host culture sensitivity training; compensation adjustment
    d. Language training; vertical integration

15. _____ eases the expatriate's adjustment to the host country.
    a. Subculture shock
    b. Monitoring and support from headquarters (easy, page 372)
    c. Reverse culture shock
    d. Repatriation

16. Common host country entry issues include all of the following except _____.
    a. motivation adjustment (moderate, page 372)
    b. departure and travel
    c. arrival and orientation
    d. on-site briefing

17. The attrition rate for expatriates is about double that of non-expatriates because
    a. Expatriates are more marketable and receive more attractive offers from other employees.
    b. Expatriates move from company to company to take advantage of more highly-compensated overseas assignments.
    c. Expatriates feel unappreciated and dissatisfied both during and after the assignment and leave the company.
    d. All of the above (moderate, pages 372-373)

18. _____ is a management skill that is likely to be learned abroad.
    a. Technical skills
    b. Information systems management
    c. Tolerance for ambiguity (moderate, page 373)
    d. Office politics

19. When a manager says "I learned to understand situations from the perspective of local employees and businesspeople," he or she is demonstrating what management skill?
   a. technical skills
   b. tolerance for ambiguity
   c. ability to work with others
   d. multiple perspectives (easy, page 373)*

20. According to Adler, which of the following are skills likely to be acquired by managers returning from an overseas alignment?
   a. tolerance for ambiguity
   b. multiple perspectives
   c. ability to work with and manage others
   d. all of the above (easy, page 373)*

21. According to research done by Black and Gregersen, which of the following was a practice used by companies that reported high degrees of job satisfaction and strong performance?
   a. They focused on knowledge creation and global leadership development.
   b. They assign overseas posts to managers who have both technical skills and cross cultural abilities.
   c. They end expatriate assignments with a deliberate repatriation process.
   d. All of the above (easy, page 373)

22. The term _____ describes collections of managers from several countries who must rely on group collaboration if each member is to experience optimum success and goal achievement.
   a. global management teams (moderate, page 374)
   b. specialized management teams
   c. virtual management teams
   d. objective management teams

23. In international firms that export and produce goods overseas, _____ play an important role in the relationship.
   a. multicultural teams (easy, page 374)
   b. third country managers
   c. sanctions
   d. repatriation policies

24. Increasingly, advances in communication now facilitate _____, with people around the world conducting meetings and exchanging information via the Internet, enabling the organization to capitalize on 24-hour productivity.
   a. virtual global teams (moderate, pages 375-376) {AACSB: Use of Information Technology}
   b. transitional global teams
   c. specialized global teams
   d. assimilated global teams

25. Which of the following is an operational challenge for a global virtual team with respect to cultural differences?
   a. variations in attitudes and expectations towards time
   b. variations in sets of norms and patterns of behavior
   c. variations in goal sets and work styles based on value of work
   d. all of the above (difficult, page 376)

26. The operational challenges for global virtual teams include all of the following except _____.
   a. geographic dispersal
   b. cultural differences
   c. language and communication
   d. exposure to different viewpoints (easy, page 376) {AACSB: Communication}

27. In a survey of 440 training and development professionals across a variety of industries by Rosen, Furst, and Blackburn, respondents indicated that the most important training needs were
   a. Training on how to lead a virtual team meeting.
   b. Leader training on how to coach and mentor team members virtually.
   c. How to monitor team progress, diagnose problems, and take corrective action.
   d. All of the above (moderate, page 376)

28. In their study of global teams, Govindarajan and Gupta found that _____.
   a. the ability to cultivate trust among team members is critical to the success of global teams (moderate, page 378) {AACSB: Communication}
   b. members of a global team must speak the same language to be successful
   c. global teams must meet at least weekly to get the task accomplished
   d. all of the above

29. Which of the following is a recommendation by Govindarajan and Gupta for improving global teamwork?
    a. link rewards to team performance
    b. rotate and diffuse team leadership
    c. rotate meeting location
    d. all of the above (easy, pages 378-379)*

30. While there are limitations on managerial opportunities for women in their own country, there are _____ for women to get expatriate assignments.
    a. unlimited opportunities
    b. no opportunities
    c. even more limitations on opportunities (easy, page 379) {AACSB: Multicultural and Diversity}
    d. about the same opportunities as for men

31. Research shows that women are _____ in expatriate assignments.
    a. disproportionately represented
    b. disproportionately underrepresented (moderate, page 379)* {AACSB: Multicultural and Diversity}
    c. overrepresented
    d. in the same proportion as men

32. Which of the following is correct about women in the Japanese workplace?
    a. The workplace has traditionally been dominated by men as far as managerial careers are concerned.
    b. Women were usually allowed only clerical positions.
    c. For the older generation, a working married woman represented a loss of face to the husband because it implied that he was unable to support her.
    d. All of the above (moderate, page 379)* {AACSB: Multicultural and Diversity}

33. While 41 percent of women work in Japan, only _____ hold managerial positions.
    a. 30.0 %
    b. 26.9%
    c. 14.3%
    d. 8.9% (difficult, page 380)* {AACSB: Multicultural and Diversity}

34. To the older generation in Japan, a working married woman _____.
    a. was a great honor
    b. represented a loss of face to the husband (moderate, page 379)* {AACSB: Multicultural and Diversity}
    c. was common for college educated women
    d. all of the above

35. Overall, more managerial opportunities are available for _____ women than for women in most other countries.
   a. German
   b. Chinese
   c. Japanese
   d. American (easy, page 380)* {AACSB: Multicultural and Diversity}

36. Yuko Suzuki, an independent business woman in Japan found that _____.
   a. her customers would not listen to her
   b. whenever she made a presentation, she was asked who her boss was
   c. when she hired a man to go with her, her sales increased significantly
   d. all of the above (moderate, page 381)* {AACSB: Multicultural and Diversity}

37. The most difficult challenge for women working overseas seems to be _____.
   a. learning how to adjust to men they must work with
   b. learning how to accept the role of women in the culture they work in
   c. getting the overseas assignment in the first place (difficult, page 383) {AACSB: Multicultural and Diversity}
   d. receiving adequate compensation for the overseas assignment

38. In _____, the disparity in opportunities for women can be traced in part to the lifestyles and laws, for example, children attend school only in the mornings which restricts the ability of both parents to work.
   a. Japan
   b. Germany (moderate, page 382-383) {AACSB: Multicultural and Diversity}
   c. Spain
   d. Italy

39. Having studied businesses operating overseas, Adler recommends that businesses _____.
   a. avoid assuming that female executives will fail because of the way she will be received abroad
   b. avoid assuming that women do no want to go abroad
   c. give female managers every chance to succeed by giving them the titles, status, and recognition appropriate to the position
   d. all of the above (moderate, page 383) {AACSB: Multicultural and Diversity}

40. Which of the following is not correct about women in international assignments?
   a. A woman who is a foreigner is not expected to act like a local woman.
   b. Asians see female executives as foreigners who happen to be women.
   c. American women can expect to be discriminated against (because they are women) in many countries (moderate, page 383)* {AACSB: Multicultural and Diversity}
   d. North American executives are reluctant to send women abroad because they assume a lack of understanding and acceptance, particularly in certain countries.

41. According to the former Deputy Chairman of Pirelli, if you want to close a plant in Italy, France, Spain, or Germany, you need to notify which of the following groups of even the possibility of closure?
   a. the state
   b. the local community
   c. the trade unions
   d. all of the above (difficult, page 383)*

42. The process through which managers and workers determine their workplace relationships is known as _____.
   a. codetermination
   b. labor relations (moderate, page 384)
   c. collective bargaining
   d. international human resources management (IHRM)

43. The labor contract generally determines _____.
   a. rights regarding workers' pay
   b. job duties
   c. firing procedures
   d. all of the above (easy, page 384)

44. One of the main dimensions of the labor-management relationship that an international manager must consider is _____.
   a. specific human resource policies in terms of recruitment, training, and compensation (easy, page 386)
   b. new international supplier talks
   c. advertising and promotional strategy
   d. all of the above

45. One of the constraints organized labor places on management is _____.
    a. limits on the repatriation of capital
    b. limits on the firm's ability to vary employment levels when necessary (difficult, page 384)*
    c. requirement to work with unions worldwide once one union contract is signed
    d. limits on hiring workers from other unions

46. Which of the following is a reason for falling union membership in industrialized countries, most notably in Europe?
    a. increase in proportion of white collar and service workers
    b. rising proportion of temporary and part-time workers
    c. reduced belief in unions by the younger generation
    d. all of the above (easy, page 384)*

47. In _____, most unions are national and represent specific groups of workers—for example truck drivers or airline pilots—so a company may have to deal with several different national unions.
    a. the United States (moderate, pages 384-385)*
    b. Japan
    c. China
    d. Europe

48. The resulting agreements from union bargaining vary around the world. A written, legally binding agreement for a specific period is common in

    _____.
    a. Southern Europe and Britain
    b. France
    c. Italy
    d. Northern Europe and North America (moderate, page 385)*

49. In _____, collective bargaining takes place between a local labor union and management.
    a. Japan
    b. the U.S. and Canada (moderate, page 385)*
    c. Europe
    d. the U.S. and Europe

50. In _____, collective bargaining takes place between the employer's organization and a trade union at the industry level.
    a. Japan
    b. the U.S.
    c. Europe (moderate, page 385)
    d. China

51.	In the U.S., union membership _____.
	a.	has been increasing and is now over 18% of the population
	b.	has been decreasing and is now only 11% of the population
	c.	is higher than in Europe, although it has decreased to 18%
	**d.	has declined about 50% in the last 20 years (difficult, page 385)**

52.	The All-China Federation of Trade Unions claimed that foreign employers

	_____.
	a.	often force workers to work overtime
	b.	pay no heed to labor safety regulations
	c.	deliberately find fault with workers as an excuse to cut wages or fine them
	**d.	all of the above (difficult, page 385)* {AACSB: Ethical Reasoning}**

53.	Some American companies are waging an intense lobbying campaign to persuade the Chinese government to revise or abandon a new proposed law. That proposed law would _____.
	a.	allow the use of prison labor in Chinese-owned factories
	b.	force U.S. firms to reveal technological secrets to local Chinese firms
	**c.	crack down on sweatshops and protect worker's rights by giving labor unions real power. (moderate, pages 386-387)* {AACSB: Ethical Reasoning}**
	d.	make child labor legal only in owned Chinese-owned factories in certain industries.

54.	Having grown increasingly concerned about the nation's widening income gap and fearing social unrest, officials in Beijing now seem determined to _____.
	**a.	improve worker protection (moderate, page 387)* {AACSB: Ethical Reasoning}**
	b.	ban labor unions which it holds responsible for rising wages in the cities
	c.	crack down on street demonstrations in the capital
	d.	increase taxes on foreign investors to pay for social programs for the rural poor

55.	All of the following are causes of convergence in labor relations practices except _____.
	a.	global competitiveness
	b.	MNC coordination among foreign subsidiaries
	c.	agencies monitoring world labor practices
	**d.	national labor relations systems and traditions (difficult, pages 388-389)**

56. _____ occurs as the migration of management and workplace practices around the world results in the reduction of workplace disparities from one country to another.
   a. **Convergence (easy, page 388)**
   b. Divergence
   c. Diversification
   d. Contradiction

57. All of the following are members of the International Labor Organization <u>except</u> _____.
   a. union leaders
   b. employers
   c. government representatives
   d. **church representatives (moderate, page 388)**

58. Which of the following is <u>not</u> a force to establish divergent labor relations systems?
   a. local and national labor relations systems and traditions
   b. **agencies monitoring world labor practices (moderate, pages 388-389)**
   c. local cultural norms
   d. All of the above are forces to establish divergent labor relations systems.

59. Currently, the only labor issues that are subject to a formal traditional review under NAFTA are _____.
   a. **minimum wages, child labor, and safety issues (difficult, page 389)* {AACSB: Ethical Reasoning}**
   b. environmental pollution, minimum wages, and child labor
   c. environmental pollution, child labor, and safety issues
   d. infant industry protection, environmental pollution, and child labor

60. Which of the following is <u>not</u> a trait of codetermination?
   a. labor participation in the management of the firm
   b. representation for unions and salaried employees on the supervisory boards of all companies
   c. **union veto power over CEO appointments (moderate, page 390)**
   d. unions can make positive contributions to corporate competitiveness and restructuring

Short Essay Questions

61. **What are the long-term consequences of an ineffective repatriation program?**

   Few good managers will be willing to take international assignments because they will see what happened to their colleagues. If a certain manager lost out on promotion opportunities while overseas and is now in fact worse off than before he or she left, the only people willing to take on foreign assignments in the future will be those who have not been able to succeed on the home front or those who think that a stint abroad will be like a vacation. In fact, research has shown that employees commonly see overseas assignments as negative career moves in many U.S. multinational companies. (moderate, page 370)*

62. **Discuss Tung's support systems to ensure a successful repatriation.**

   Tung offers the following recommendations: 1) a mentor program to monitor the expatriate's career path while abroad and upon repatriation; 2) as an alternative to the mentor program, the establishment of a special organizational unit for the purposes of career planning and continuing guidance for the expatriate; and, 3) a system of supplying information and maintaining contacts with the expatriate so that he or she may continue to feel a part of the home organization. (moderate, page 371)

63. **Give examples of what firms have done to help dual-career couples adjust to international assignments.**

   At Procter & Gamble, employees and spouses destined for China are sent to Beijing for two months of language training and cultural familiarization. At Nissho Iwai, a Japanese trading company, managers and spouses who are leaving Japan get together with managers and spouses who are heading there. In addition, the firm provides a year of language training and information and services for Japanese children to attend schools abroad. (moderate, page 371)*

64. **What three transitions must a company manage if its expatriate managers are to be successful?**

   The three transitions are: 1) the exit transition from the home country, the success of which will be determined primarily by the quality of preparation received by the expatriate; 2) the entry transition to the host country, in which successful acculturation or early exit will depend mostly on monitoring and support; and 3) the entry transition back to the home country or a new host country, in which the level of reverse culture shock and the ease of re-acculturation will depend on previous stages of preparation and support. (moderate, page 372)

65. **List three specific practices that were used by U.S., European, and Japanese companies which reported a high degree of job satisfaction and strong performance based on research by Black and Gregersen.**
(1) They focus on knowledge creation and global leadership development, (2) they assign overseas posts to people whose technical skills are matched or exceeded by their cross-cultural abilities, and (3) they end expatriate assignments with a deliberate repatriation process. (moderate, page 373)*

66. **What are some of the operational challenges for global virtual teams with respect to language and communication?**
Since the teams comprise of members from different nationalities and culture, there are translation difficulties especially with respect to accents, semantics, terminology and jargon. Lack of personal and physical contact inhibits trust and relationship building which is necessary in many countries before members feel comfortable working with one another. Also the lack of visibility of non-verbal cues makes interpretation difficult and results in two-way noise in the communication process. (moderate, page 376)*

67. **Discuss the conflicts associated with transnational teams.**
Teams comprising people located in far flung operations are faced with conflicting goals of achieving greater efficiency across those operations, responding to local differences, and facilitating organizational learning. Conflicts arise based on cultural differences, local work norms, and environments, and varied time zones. A study by Joshi revealed that the greatest conflicts did not result from the headquarters-subsidiary power divide, but rather between subsidiaries given the required communication and workflow patterns between them. (difficult, page 377)*

68. **What can companies do to take more advantage of women as a resource for international management?**
Primarily, companies should avoid three assumptions: They should not assume that the assignment of a woman will not work out successfully; they should not assume that a woman will not want to go overseas; they should give women managers every chance to succeed through giving them an adequate title, status, and compensation. (easy, page 383)* {AACSB: Multicultural and Diversity}

69. **What are the three main dimensions of the international labor-management relationship?**
The three main dimensions of the labor-management relationship which the manager will consider are: (1) the participation of labor in the affairs of the firm, especially as this affects performance and well-being; (2) the role and impact of unions in the relationship; and (3) specific human-resource policies in terms of recruitment, training, and compensation. (moderate, page 384)

70. **What constraints does organized labor place on an international manager?**
Constraints take the form of (1) wage levels which are set by union contracts and leave the foreign firm little flexibility to be globally competitive; (2) limits on the ability of the foreign firm to vary employment levels when necessary; (3) limitations on the global integration of operations of the foreign firm because of incompatibility and the potential for industrial conflict.   (moderate, page 384)*

71. **To what extent are Western Europeans covered by labor agreements? Compare this to the U.S.**
Most Europeans are covered by labor agreements while most Americans are not. The percentage of trade unions in industrialized countries has declined in the last decade, most notably in Europe. Despite this recent decline, however, union membership in Europe is still quite high, particularly in Italy and the United Kingdom. In contrast, in the United States, union membership fell from a third in 1950 to about 12% in 2006. (difficult, pages 384-385)*

72. **Discuss the differences in collective bargaining in the U.S. and Canada and Europe?**
In the U.S. and Canada, collective bargaining refers to negotiations between a local labor union and management, but in Europe, collective bargaining takes place between the employer's organization and a trade union at the industry level. This means that North America's decentralized, plant-level, collective agreements are more detailed than Europe's industry-wide agreements because of the myriad of details involved in multi-employer bargaining. (moderate, page 385)*

73. **Discuss the issues of convergence vs. divergence in labor systems.**
Convergence is the phenomenon of increasing similarity in labor relations practices across borders as a result of common external practices and the moves of MNCs across national borders. Convergence occurs primarily as MNCs seek consistency and coordination among their foreign subsidiaries and as they act as catalysts for change by "exporting" new forms of work organization and industrial relations practices. Divergence is the phenomenon of increasing differences in labor relations practices as a result of national, political, economic, or cultural considerations. MNCs still adapt their practices largely to the traditions of national industrial relations systems. The pressures for convergence are stronger than those for divergence. (moderate, pages 388-389)

Comprehensive Essay Questions

74. **Explain why effective human resource management of a company's global cadre does not end with the overseas assignment?**

Effective human resource management of a firm's global cadre does not end with the overseas assignment. It ends with the successful repatriation of the executive back to the company headquarters, and the integration of that executive into the company's global management cadre. The development of this global management cadre is a central component of successful human resource management. When an executive returns from an overseas assignment, that executive becomes part of the mechanism to develop other managers with international experience. In order for this to occur, the returning executive must be successfully reintegrated into the organization, and his or her skills must be made available to other managers contemplating international assignments. Also, that manager's career should not be adversely affected by the overseas assignment. The overall goal is to have this experienced manager serve as a leader in developing the global management cadre over a period of time in the organization. (moderate, pages 369-371)

75. **Discuss the role of "reverse culture shock" in the repatriation process. What can companies do to avoid this problem?**

Management of the reentry phase of the career cycle is as vital as management of the cross-cultural entry and training. Many expatriates and their families have a difficult time readjusting to their old culture and its different behavioral expectations. The longer the person is away, the more difficult it is for them to reintegrate into the organization and get back into the swing of things. The family may have lost social contacts or jobs and feel out of step with their contemporaries. There may be feelings of alienation from what was perceived as home. A mentor-mentee program is perhaps the best method for companies to use in avoiding the reverse culture problem. Keeping the employee informed about company news and development while he is on assignment abroad can also help ease the strain and stress of coming back. Many companies make plans ahead of time assuring the expatriate manager what role he will assume on his return- such long term planning can go a long way in minimizing the reverse culture shock the returning manager is likely to face and will help retain the manager with the company who may otherwise be tempted to seek another job opportunity. (moderate, page 370)*

76. **What are the skills a manager learns abroad? In your opinion, why wouldn't U.S. managers learn these skills at the home office?**

Four general sets of skills that are likely to be learned abroad:

1) Managerial rather than technical skills: learning how to deal with a wide variety of people, to adapt to their cultures, and to not impose your cultural values upon them.

2) Tolerance for ambiguity: making decisions with limited information and more uncertainty about the process and the outcome.

3) Multiple perspectives: learning to understand situations from the perspective of local employees and businesspeople.

4) Ability to work with and manage others: learning patience and tolerance – realizing that managers abroad are in the minority among local people; learning to communicate more with others and empathize with them.

Why wouldn't U.S. managers learn these skills at the home office? Few companies have the diversity in-house that an employee would encounter overseas. This in-depth immersion into cultural diversity requires a major adjustment on the part of the expatriate manager. In the home country, managers may be able to succeed without making this adjustment. In an overseas assignment, there is no option – managers adjust or they fail. (moderate, page 373)*

Chapter 11
Motivating and Leading

Multiple Choice Questions

1. In order to motivate its managers and employees, Fujitsu _____.
    a. tied pay to performance
    b. raised the incentive pay
    c. cut managers' salaries by several percent (easy, page 398)*
    d. all of the above

2. _____ suggests the need for job security, whereas people with _____ would probably be motivated by more risky opportunities for variety and fast-track advancement.
    a. High uncertainty avoidance; low uncertainty avoidance (moderate, page 399)
    b. Low uncertainty avoidance; high uncertainty avoidance
    c. Large power distance; small power distance
    d. Small power distance; large power distance

3. People in highly individualistic countries such as the United States are likely to be motivated by _____.
    a. opportunities for individual advancement and autonomy (easy, page 399)*
    b. appeals to group goals
    c. rewards that are collective rather than individualistic
    d. all of the above

4. _____ suggests that most people would be more comfortable with the traditional division of work and roles; in a _____ culture, the boundaries could be looser, motivating people through more flexible roles and work networks.
    a. High masculinity; more feminine (moderate, page 399)
    b. A more feminine culture; masculine
    c. High uncertainty avoidance; low uncertainty avoidance
    d. Low uncertainty; high uncertainty

5. For most people, the basic meaning of work refers to _____.
    a. self-fulfillment
    b. self-identity
    c. team or group membership
    d. economic necessity (moderate, page 400)

6. According to a study by Steers, Koreans' hard work was attributable to _____.
    a. loyalty to the company
    b. group-oriented achievement
    c. emphasis on group harmony and business relationships
    d. all of the above (easy, page 401)*

7. The degree of general importance that working has in the life of an individual is called _____.
    a. intrinsic motivation
    b. extrinsic motivation
    c. need paradigm
    d. work centrality (moderate, page 401)

8. Which two sets of needs are identified in the Herzberg model?
    a. productivity and nonproductivity factors
    b. satisfiers and hygiene factors
    c. motivators and maintenance factors (moderate, page 391)
    d. motivators and group factors

9. Which of the following is a factor identified in the Meaning of Work (MOW) research study?
    a. work keeps one occupied
    b. work provides a needed income
    c. work provides contacts with others
    d. all of the above (moderate, page 401)

10. Which of the following nations ranked highest in the centrality of work according to the Meaning of Work research study?
    a. U.S.
    b. Netherlands
    c. Belgium
    d. Japan (moderate, page 401)*

11. According to the text, Ronen concludes that _____ are constant across nationalities and that Maslow's need hierarchy is confirmed by those clusters.
    a. need clusters (difficult, page 403)
    b. value clusters
    c. behavioral clusters
    d. moral clusters

12. According to Ronen's research, which of the following are common clusters of needs and goals across nationalities?
    a. job goals
    b. relationships with co-workers and supervisors
    c. work challenges and opportunities for using skills
    d. all of the above (easy, page 403)

13. While American companies tend to stress individual goals, achievement, and rewards, Japanese companies tend to stress _____.
    a. financial goals
    b. financial rewards for teams
    c. group wide goals (moderate, pages 403-404)
    d. status recognition

14. Nevis proposes that the hierarchy of Chinese needs would be such that the first need would be _____.
    a. physiological
    b. belonging (moderate, page 405)*
    c. safety
    d. self-actualization in the service of society

15. Which of the following is <u>not</u> an extrinsic motivational factor?
    a. relations with others
    b. the work itself (easy, page 405)
    c. fairness in organizational practices
    d. personal problems

16. Kanungo and Wright recommend that efforts to improve managerial performance in the U.K. should focus on _____.
    a. job content (moderate, page 405)*
    b. job context
    c. security
    d. fringe benefits

17. Which of the following does <u>not</u> accurately characterize workers in the Mexican culture?
    a. They rank high on power distance.
    b. They rank high on uncertainty avoidance.
    c. They rank low on individualism.
    d. All of the above characterize Mexican workers. (difficult, page 406)*
        {AACSB: Multicultural and Diversity}

18. In Mexico, _____ is of central importance.
    a. participation in decision making
    b. informality
    c. individualism
    d. family (easy, page 406)* {AACSB: Multicultural and Diversity}

19.   Which of the following is the most common reason given for absenteeism among Mexican workers?
       a. illness
       b. taking care of sick relatives and elderly parents (moderate, page 406)* {AACSB: Multicultural and Diversity}
       c. dissatisfaction with the job
       d. personal problems

20.   According to a U.S expatriate, Mexican workers need more _____ than US workers.
       a. pay
       b. relationship building (easy, page 407)* {AACSB: Multicultural and Diversity}
       c. benefits
       d. autonomy

21.   The _____ management style works best in Mexico.
       a. democratic
       b. authoritative (easy, page 407)* {AACSB: Multicultural and Diversity}
       c. consensus
       d. rational

22.   Which of the following are suggestions for implementing work teams in Mexico?
       a. provide leadership from the top throughout the implementation process
       b. develop motivation and harmony through clear expectations
       c. provide adequate training to prepare workers for teamwork
       d. all of the above (moderate, page 408)* {AACSB: Multicultural and Diversity}

23.   In Michailova's study, Russian employees were more motivated by the _____ of their Russian managers than by attempts of empowerment by Western managers.
       a. authoritarianism (moderate, page 409)*
       b. patriarchy
       c. autonomy
       d. pluralism

24.   Whereas Americans believe that hard work will get the job done, many Hong Kong Chinese believe that outcomes will be determined by _____.
       a. family
       b. social standing
       c. luck (moderate, page 409)* {AACSB: Multicultural and Diversity}
       d. education

25. In Taiwan, the most highly sought reward is _____.
    a. pay
    b. security
    c. recognition from peers
    d. **recognition from the top and affection (moderate, page 410) {AACSB: Multicultural and Diversity}**

26. Which of the following is <u>not</u> among the five categories of rewards typical in the American culture?
    a. job content
    b. **self-fulfillment (moderate, page 410) {AACSB: Multicultural and Diversity}**
    c. career
    d. social status

27. In China, the plaque award "Ms. Wong- employee of the Month" was given to _____.
    a. recognize Ms. Wong as the best employee of the month
    b. recognize the best saleswoman of the month
    c. **shame the worst employee of the month (moderate, page 410)* {AACSB: Multicultural and Diversity}**
    d. Ms. Wong because it was her turn in the rotation.

28. Which of the following is <u>not</u> one of the four personal development strategies (four "t's") through which companies and managers can meet the requirements of effective global leadership?
    a. through travel
    b. through teamwork
    c. through training
    d. **through technology (difficult, page 411)**

29. Effective _____ involves the ability to inspire and influence the thinking, attitudes, and behavior of people anywhere in the world.
    a. **global leadership (moderate, page 411)**
    b. ethnocentric leadership
    c. polycentric leadership
    d. virtual leadership

30. According to Mason and Spich, the leader's role is an interaction of which two sets of variables?
    a. **content and context (difficult, page 412)**
    b. personal and professional
    c. internal and external
    d. cultural and societal

31. Since effective leadership traits vary with the situation and with the followers according to each context, the idea of _____ is not valid.
    a. predictive leadership models
    b. leadership definitions
    c. understanding leadership in different cultures
    d. universal leadership traits (difficult, page 414)*

32. In Latin American countries, leaders are respected as _____.
    a. people possessing machismo
    b. bosses in total authority
    c. representatives of workers
    d. multidimensional social beings (difficult, page 414)*

33. The _____ model of leadership style has been recommended by American research studies as one more likely to have positive results with American employees.
    a. autocratic
    b. charismatic
    c. transactional
    d. democratic (moderate, page 414)* {AACSB: Multicultural and Diversity}

34. Which of the following is <u>not</u> a leadership style and behavior that was found to be culturally contingent?
    a. charismatic
    b. participative
    c. autonomous
    d. trustworthy (difficult, page 414)* {AACSB: Multicultural and Diversity}

35. Which of the following is <u>not</u> a leadership style and behavior that was found to be generally accepted anywhere (i.e., universally considered facilitators of leadership effectiveness?
    a. trustworthy
    b. charismatic (difficult, page 414)
    c. effective bargainer
    d. skilled administrator and communicator

36. Which of the following is not a leadership style that is universally considered an impediment to leadership effectiveness?
    a. uncooperative
    b. egocentric
    c. ruthless
    d. self-protective (moderate, page 414)

37. The _____ leader is someone who is, for example, a visionary, an inspiration to subordinates, and performance-oriented.
    a. charismatic (easy, page 416)
    b. team-oriented
    c. participative
    d. self-protective

38. A _____ leader is someone who exhibits diplomatic, integrative, and collaborative behaviors towards the team.
    a. charismatic
    b. team-oriented (moderate, page 416)
    c. participative
    d. self-protective

39. The _____ dimension describes a leader who is self-centered, conflictual, and status conscious.
    a. charismatic
    b. team-oriented
    c. participative
    d. self-protective (moderate, page 416)

40. The _____ leader is one who delegates decision making and encourages subordinates to take responsibility.
    a. charismatic
    b. team-oriented
    c. participative (easy, page 416)
    d. self-protective

41. According to Hofstede, employees in countries that rank high on power distance are more likely to prefer a(n) _____ leadership style.
    a. autocratic (moderate, page 416)
    b. participative
    c. charismatic
    d. transformational

42. Employees in countries that rank low on power distance are more likely to prefer a(n) _____ leadership style.
    a. autocratic
    b. participative (moderate, page 416)
    c. charismatic
    d. transformational

43. According to Hofstede, the critical fact to grasp about leadership in any culture is that it is a complement to _____.
   a. the leader's personality
   b. the needs of the leader's boss
   c. the demands placed on the leader by the organization
   d. subordinateship (moderate, pages 416-417)

44. In a large power distance society, subordinates _____.
   a. expect superiors to act autocratically (difficult, page 416)*
   b. have weak dependence needs
   c. expect superiors to be resourceful democrats
   d. frown upon status symbols

45. Laurent concluded that _____ significantly affects the perception of what is effective management.
   a. educational background of followers
   b. type of organization structure in place
   c. the needs of subordinates
   d. national origin (moderate, page 418)*

46. Managers in Sweden, the Netherlands, U.S., Denmark, and Great Britain seem to believe that employees prefer which style of leadership?
   a. autocratic
   b. charismatic
   c. participative (moderate, page 418)*
   d. laissez faire

47. In the Middle East, leaders are expected to _____.
   a. show a highly authoritarian tone
   b. give rigid instructions
   c. provide too many management directives
   d. all of the above (moderate, page 411)* {AACSB: Multicultural and Diversity}

48. A survey of 200 chief executives in France, Germany, and the United Kingdom concluded that_____,
   a. a common leadership style is feasible for 25 of the 27 E.U. members
   b. a common leadership style for all E.U. countries is not feasible (moderate, page 421)*
   c. a common leadership style is feasible for France and Germany, but not the United Kingdom
   d. a common leadership style is feasible for all countries except France

49. A survey of 200 chief executives in France, Germany, and the United Kingdom concluded that _____.
     a. the French are more likely than the British and Germans to regard being in a position of power as being important
     b. French leaders like to make decisions unilaterally
     c. leaders in the United Kingdom seemed less troubled about their decisions
     d. all of the above are correct (difficult, page 421)*

50. The status of leaders in France is based primarily on_____.
     a. the companies that they lead
     b. how much wealth they have accumulated
     c. their position and the educational institutions that they attended (moderate, page 422)* {AACSB: Multicultural and Diversity}
     d. the size of the firms that they lead

Short Essay Questions

51. **What is the concept of work centrality and how is it important to cross cultural management?**
     The concept measures the central importance of work as a motivating factor in a person's life. The centrality of work will greatly influence both the content and process of motivation. The higher the mean work centrality score, the more motivated and committed workers will be. (moderate, page 401)* {AACSB: **Multicultural and Diversity}**

52. **What attributes did the MOW group consider when they investigated cross-cultural motivation.**
     The MOW research looked at the extent to which work satisfied the following six functions: 1) work provides a needed income; 2) work is interesting and satisfying; 3) work permits interesting contacts with others; 5) work facilitates a way to serve society; 5) work keeps one occupied, and 5) work gives status and prestige. (moderate, page 401) {AACSB: **Multicultural and Diversity}**

53. **What hierarchy did Nevis propose to replace Maslow in the Chinese culture?**
     Nevis found a different order for Chinese: (1) belonging, (2) physiological needs, (3) safety, and (4) self-actualization in the service of society. While the categories are similar, the Chinese have a different motivational hierarchy than the hierarchy predicted by Maslow. (moderate, page 405)* {AACSB: **Multicultural and Diversity}**

54. **What is the distinction between intrinsic and extrinsic motivation?**
Intrinsic needs come from within the individual, such as the opportunity for growth and the nature of the work. Extrinsic factors include conditions that surround the job such as relations with others and fairness in organizational practices, rather than characteristics of the job itself. According to research, work motivation tends to result from intrinsic needs, whereas dissatisfaction tends to result from extrinsic factors. (moderate, page 405)

55. **Identify five things that are important to Mexican workers, and that will affect their behavior at work.**
1) In Mexico, the family is of prime importance, so a worker might be absent because he or she needs to care for a sick relative. Workers may also not return to work after a vacation or holiday.
2) Since Mexican culture is high uncertainty avoidance, Mexican workers prefer security and formality over risk. The best management style will be authoritative and paternal.
3) Mexican workers expect to be treated in a respectful (formal) manner. They need more communication, more relationship-building, and more reassurance than American employees.
4) Maslow's higher-order needs would not be motivators for most Mexicans. Instead, money (bonuses) and fringe benefits will be of greater importance.
5) Since workers highly value the enjoyment of life, many companies in Mexico provide recreational facilities such a picnic area and a soccer field.
(moderate, pages 406-408)* {AACSB: Multicultural and Diversity}

56. **List the four development strategies recommended by Morrison, Gregersen, and Black through which companies and managers can meet the requirements of effective global leadership.**
The four personal development strategies through which companies and managers can meet the requirements of effective global leadership are: travel, teamwork, training, and transfers. (moderate, page 411)

57. **Distinguish between leadership content and context.**
Content comprises the attributes of the leader (e.g., knowledge, position, and expectations) and the characteristics of decisions to be made (e.g., the degree of complexity, uncertainty, and risk). In contrast, the context of leadership refers to the attributes of the job or position (e.g., the technical requirements of the job) and the characteristics of the firm and business environment (e.g., the size of the firm, the political-economic aspects of the country or market) (difficult, page 412)

58. **List any four of the six roles which managers on international assignments have to juggle in order to maximize leadership effectiveness.**
The six roles include (1) a representative of the parent firm, (2) the manager of the local firm, (3) a resident of the local community, (4) a citizen of either the host country or of another country, (5) a member of a profession, and (6) a member of a family. (moderate, page 412)

59. **Which dimension (or dimensions) of leadership style is the focus of most U.S. research? Which leadership style is more likely to have positive results with U.S. employees?**
Most research on U.S. leadership styles describe managerial behaviors on basically the same dimension variously termed autocratic versus democratic; participative versus directive; relations-oriented versus task-oriented; initiating structure versus consideration. The studies from which these dimensions were derived largely reflect the opinions of U.S. workers. The democratic or participative style ids most likely to have positive results with U.S. employees (moderate, page 414)

60. **List the six leadership styles and behaviors that were found to be culturally contingent based on the research conducted by the GLOBE project.**
The six leadership styles and behaviors are (1) charismatic, (2) team-oriented, (3) self-protective, (4) participative, (5) humane, and (6) autonomous. (moderate, page 414)

61. **What is subordinateship? What are the characteristics of subordinateship in large power distance countries?**
Subordinateship revolves around employees' attitudes toward leaders, and how employees act based upon those attitudes. Subordinateship varies depending on whether the culture is small, medium, or large power distance. The characteristics of subordinateship in large power distance countries are as follows: subordinates have strong dependence needs, expect their superiors to act autocratically, view an ideal superior as a benevolent autocrat, expect superiors to enjoy privileges, accept that laws and rules differ for subordinates and superiors, and that status symbols are important. (moderate, page 417)*

Comprehensive Essay Questions

62. **Is it appropriate to use the same leadership style across all EU countries, or should the style vary?**

    Most research shows that there are differences in leadership style across EU countries, and hence a single style would not be feasible. Given the different histories, languages, government systems, business practices, educational systems, religions, organizations, and cultures, a single leadership style would not work. This position is supported by a survey of 200 chief executives in France, Germany, and the United Kingdom in which executives argued that a single style was not feasible. This study labeled the French captains of industry as "autocrats", the Germans as "democrats", and the British as "meritocrats". This survey also found that while French leaders like to make decisions unilaterally, German executives indicated their concern about the responsibility of their decisions. In contrast, leaders in the United Kingdom seemed less troubled about their decisions. Other research also supports differences in leadership styles across these three countries.

    Is having different leadership styles across countries undesirable? This seems to be the suggestion of Kets de Vries and Korotov based on their research. They argue that while the Japanese and Americans can have a "local" leadership style, the option is not feasible in the EU because of the blending of labor, goods, and services and processes across the EU countries. These researchers argue that an "EU style" that will work across all EU countries is needed. (difficult, page 421)*

63. **Would Japanese motivation practices work with U.S. employees? Are some more applicable than others? Can we conclude that they are applicable across cultures, or does it depend on the situation? Discuss your conclusion.**

    While the Japanese emphasis on sense of identify derived mainly from work (they have a high score on the Meaning of Work scale) would appear to be appealing to many American workers, one must be careful not to assume that all Japanese motivational techniques would be as effective. Because Americans are much more individualistic in their motivational profile, the Japanese emphasis on subordination of self to the group would not work as effectively in the United States as it does in Japan. For example, in the United States, rewards are given individually and primarily based on merit. In Japan, however, rewards are based on seniority and rewarding the individual is frowned upon as it encourages competition. As numerous research studies have concluded, one must be very careful in over-generalizing about universal motivational appeals across cultures. (difficult, pages 400-401, 410)* {**AACSB: Multicultural and Diversity**}

64. **Discuss Herzberg's two-factor theory of motivation as it relates to different countries around the world. What can we conclude and use in management, regarding this theory?**

A review of research shows some support for Herzberg's two-factor theory (motivators versus satisfiers) among different countries of the world. This allows us to draw tentative conclusions that managers around the world are motivated more by intrinsic rather than by extrinsic factors. However, there remains considerable doubt about the universality of Herzberg's theory because it is not possible to take into consideration all the relevant cultural variables when researching motivation. (moderate, page 406)*

65. **Discuss the six suggestions provided by Mexican executives surveyed regarding the implementation of work teams.**

The six suggestions are: (1) foster a culture of individual responsibility among team members; (2) anticipate the impact of changes in power distribution; (3) provide leadership from the top throughout the implementation process; (4) provide adequate training to prepare workers for team work; (5) develop motivation and harmony through clear expectations; and (6) encourage an environment of shared responsibility. (moderate, page 408)* {**AACSB: Multicultural and Diversity**}

SAMPLE EXAMS

Exam 1: Chapters 1-4

*ANSWER **FOUR** OF THE FOLLOWING FIVE QUESTIONS (5 POINTS EACH).*

Be sure to give full, comprehensive answers with enough detail to convince the reader that you understand the concepts. Be sure that your answer demonstrates knowledge and understanding of the course and text. Use subheadings and bulleted lists as appropriate.

1. **Explain the terms ethnocentrism, ethical relativism, and moral universalism, as they pertain to the social responsibility actions of MNCs. Is one approach preferred over another?** (Chapter 2, pages 36-41)

   The term "ethnocentrism" refers to the attitude of MNCs which operate from the assumption that their ways of doing things are best- no matter where or under what conditions they are applied. Under the ethnocentric approach, an MNC applies the morality used in its home country- regardless of the host country's system of ethics. For example, while Americans consider it unethical to employ child labor and have strict laws prohibiting it, child labor occurs in other countries as a source of cheap labor for firms and a means to supplement the family's income.

   Under "ethical relativism", the company simply adopts the local moral code of the country in which it is operating (e.g., "When in Rome, do as the Romans do"). With this approach, companies run into value conflicts, for example, where companies continue to export silicone-filled breast implants (prohibited in the United States for health reasons). Companies such as Dow Corning have ceased foreign sales of breast implants citing its responsibility to apply the same standards internationally as it does domestically (in essence taking both an ethnocentric and universalist stance).

   Under "moral universalism" the company adheres to the same standards of ethical behavior in every part of the world where it operates. Moral universalism also implies that the MNCs adhere to a set of universal moral principles rather than principles derived from its home or host country. For example, certain minimum standards of human rights, labor rights, and concern for the environment fall within the category of "moral universalism".

   A specific example of universal standards or principles used by MNCs is the Social Accountability 8000 (SA 8000). These are standards modeled on the manufacturing standard ISO 8000. The SA8000 proposes the following:

   - Do not use child or forced labor
   - Provide a safe working environment
   - Respect worker's rights to unionize
   - Do not regularly require more then 48-hour work weeks

- Pay sufficient wages to cover worker's basic needs
- These standards would fall under "moral universalism"

Other examples of universal standards are the International Codes of Conduct for MNEs discussed in Chapter 3. These codes were developed by the International Chamber of Commerce, the Organization for Economic Cooperation and Development, the International Labor Organization, and the United Nations. These organizations have promulgated codes of conduct for MNCs in areas such as technology transfer, consumer protection, employment practices, human rights, and other areas.

Is one approach preferred over another? According to Bowie, the moral universalism approach is preferable to the ethnocentrism or moral relativism approaches.

2. **a) Define and explain the term societal culture.** (Chapter 3, pages 91-92)

Societal culture (or, the culture of a society) comprises the shared values, understandings, assumptions, and goals that are learned from earlier generations, imposed by present members of the society and are passed on to succeeding generations. Essentially, societal culture is learned and shared by and among members of that society. There are several variable components of culture that determine attitudes of people towards work, time, materialism, individualism, and change. For example in U.S. culture, one is expected to be on time for appointments unlike some cultures where time is viewed as flexible.

b) Give examples of operational conflicts that could occur in a cross-cultural context because of different attitudes toward: 1) time, 2) change, 3) individualism. (Give of a country or region that would be different from the United States for each of the three variables). (Chapter 3, pages 105-107)

Time: In many parts of the world time is looked upon on a different and longer perspective than in the United States. Americans tend to view time as a valuable limited resource to be spent, saved and used judiciously. Time is precious and deadlines and schedules are not only important but are crucial in business situations. There are however, contrasting perspectives about time. For example, in Latin America, a common attitude towards time is *mañana* which usually means an indefinite time in the future. Similarly, the word *bukra* in Arabic can mean "tomorrow," or "some time in the future." While Americans usually regard a deadline as a firm commitment, Arabs often regard a deadline imposed on them as an insult. They feel that important things take a long time and should not be rushed.

Change: The attitude towards change is directly related to a society's belief in the extent to which it can control the future. Western societies generally believe that an individual can exert some control over the future and can manipulate events, particularly in a business context. In contrast, in many non-Western societies, people believe that their destiny is under the control of external events, or the will of their God. The managerial implications of this cultural characteristic are that while Americans or other westerners believe that they can change themselves as individuals (e.g., improve their abilities as a leader), other societies may not believe such change is possible. Americans may also be more likely to hold individuals responsible for creating change in an organization (e.g., improving performance), whereas other societies with place less faith in the ability of an individual to bring about such change.

Individualism: Americans are high on "individualism"- they value individual achievement, accomplishments, and rewards highly. In contrast, certain societies (e.g., China) place emphasis on group goals and group achievement. In China, a much more "we" consciousness prevails, and the group is the basic building block of social life and work. For the Chinese, conformity and cooperation take precedence over individual achievement, and the emphasis is on the strength of the family or community.

3. **Explain each of Hofstede's four culture dimensions (individualism, uncertainty avoidance, power distance, masculinity), and discuss the managerial implications of each. Give examples of countries that have each of the values.** (Chapter 3 , pages 100-103)

Hofstede's model of the four dimensions that underlie organization behavior are as follows:

Power distance: is defined as the level of acceptance by society of the unequal distribution of power in institutions. In countries in which people display a high power distance (such as Malaysia, the Philippines, and Mexico) employees accept the boss's authority and they seldom bypass the chain of command. In such societies, an autocratic management style is expected and works well. In low power distance societies (such as Austria, Denmark, and Israel), superiors and subordinates regard each other as equal. In such societies, a more democratic style is expected and works well.

Uncertainty avoidance: refers to the extent to which people in a society feel threatened by ambiguous situations. People in societies where uncertainty avoidance is high (such as Japan, Portugal, and Greece) tend to be highly risk averse and there is a greater resistance to change than in societies where uncertainty avoidance is low. Managers in these societies tend to use more rules and procedures, employees are less aggressive, and lifetime employment is common. In countries with low uncertainty avoidance (such as Denmark, Great Britain, and to a lesser extent, the United States) company activities are less structured, and less formal, managers take more risks, and high job mobility is common.

Individualism: refers to the tendency of people to look after themselves and their immediate family only and to neglect the needs of society. In individualist societies (such as the United States, Great Britain, and Australia), democracy, individual initiative, and achievement are highly valued. In collectivist societies (such as Japan, Pakistan and Panama), the group needs takes precedence over individual will. Collectivist societies value harmony, saving face, and emphasize the group in decision making.

Masculinity: refers to the degree to which traditionally masculine values such as assertiveness, materialism and lack of concern for others prevail in a society. Femininity emphasizes a concern for others, for relationships, and for quality of life. In highly masculine societies (such as Japan and Austria), there is more job stress and organizational interests generally encroach on employees private lives. In contrast, in countries with low masculinity (such as Switzerland and New Zealand), there is less conflict and job stress, more women in high-level jobs, and reduced need for assertiveness. The United States lies somewhere in-between masculinity and femininity. American women are encouraged to work, and families are often able to get some support for child care.

4. **a) Explain the differences in communication styles between high-context and low-context cultures, giving a country or regional example for each.** (Chapter 4, page 135)

In high-context cultures (countries in Asia, the Middle East, Africa and the Mediterranean), feelings and thoughts are not explicitly expressed; instead one has to read between the lines and interpret meaning from one's general understanding. Key information is embedded in the context rather than clearly stated. People make assumptions about the message based on the background information they have about the person based on personal ties and knowledge of the person or surroundings.

In low context cultures (Germany, United States, Switzerland, Scandinavia) business and personal relationships are more compartmentalized and communication is more explicit. Feelings and thoughts are expressed clearly in words and information is readily available.

b) Explain why these differences often cause "noise" in communication between Americans and Arabs. (Chapter 4, pages 137-138)

Arabs and Americans differ vastly in communication styles based in the fact that they come from very high and low context cultures respectively. Often these styles can cause "noise".

Middle Eastern culture emphasizes friendship, honor, religion and traditional hospitality. Family, friends, and connections are very important and take precedence over business transactions. Giving and receiving favors and being interrupted by friends and family during a business meeting may be common for an Arab but highly distracting for an American who may construe that the Arab does not consider the matter important enough to give it his full and undivided attention.

Not only is the Arab culture high-context, it is also a high contact culture. Arabs stand and sit closer together and touch people of the same sex more often than Americans do. The distance preferred by Americans, the concept of maintaining their personal space bubble, may offend the Arab as being stand-offish.

A typical culture clash occurs when an American tries to give an Arab a strict deadline- the Arab's attitude to time is derived from the Muslim expression "Bukra insha Allah" meaning "Tomorrow if Allah wills" and the Arab feels insulted and considers the American rude, pushy and demanding.

Again, Arabs coming from high-context cultures tend to meander, start business with social talk, discuss business for a while, then loop around to social issues and then again come back to business. Americans being used to a direct, linear and explicit form of communication often feel impatient and confused by this communication style.

5. **Explain the broad differences in communication style between Japanese and Americans. Then, give some specific examples of that would contrast the Japanese *ningensei* style with the more adversarial American style.** (Chapter 4, pages 140-141)

The Japanese *ningensei* or "human beingness" style of communication refers to the preference for humanity, reciprocity, a receiver orientation, and an underlying distrust of words and analytic logic. The Japanese believe that true intentions are not necessarily contained in words or contracts, but instead masked by them. In contrast to the typical American's verbal agility and explicitness, Japanese communicate with the goal of defending and giving face for everyone concerned. In particular, the Japanese will avoid public disagreements.

Some specific examples of the contrasting styles are given below:

Japanese	American
1. Indirect verbal and nonverbal communication.	More direct verbal and nonverbal communication.
2. Relationship communication.	More task communication.
3. Strategically ambiguous communication.	Prefers more to-the-point communication.
4. Delayed feedback.	More immediate feedback
5. Uses fewer words.	Favors verbosity.

Exam 2: Chapters 5-8

ANSWER ALL OF THE FOUR QUESTIONS (five points each).

Be sure to give full, comprehensive answers with enough detail to convince the reader that you understand the concepts. Be sure that your answer demonstrates knowledge and understanding of the course and text. Use subheadings and bulleted lists as appropriate.

1. **Explain three important characteristics of the Chinese culture that affect the negotiation process. Be sure to explain how these characteristics affect the negotiation process. Then, explain three important negotiating styles and expectations of the Chinese that you need to be aware of when negotiating in China.** (Chapter 5, pages 167-170)

There are three important Chinese cultural norms that affect the negotiation process: ingrained politeness and emotional restraint, emphasis on social obligation, and belief in the interconnection of work, family, and friendship. These cultural norms affect the negotiation process as follows. Because of the Chinese preference for emotional restraint and saving face, attempts at persuasion in negotiation are likely to fail. The concept of face is central to this kind of response. Face has two components- *lien* (a person's moral character) and *mein-tsu* (a person's reputation). Americans have to be careful in negotiations to not make it obvious that they have "won" so that the Chinese do not lose face. It is recommended to make token concessions and other attempts to show respect. The cultural emphasis on social obligation means that appeals to individual members of the Chinese negotiation team will likely backfire. Finally, the interconnection of work, family, and friendship is manifested through *guanxi* – the intricate network of personal relationships that permeates all business relationships including negotiation.

Some important negotiating styles and expectations of the Chinese negotiation are:

- The Chinese will require a lot of detail about product characteristics.
- Chinese negotiators typically have little authority to make decisions.
- The Chinese negotiating team is usually about twice as large as the Western team.
- The Chinese will employ tactics such as delaying and the avoidance of direct, specific answers.
- Older and more experienced people are more acceptable to the Chinese in cross-cultural negotiations.
- The Chinese like to deal with top executives of American companies because of the assumption that such managers reached the top by fostering close relationships and building trust among their colleagues.

2. **a) List the eight international entry strategies in your text, in order of ascending risk (without explanation), and note a critical success factor beside each.** (Chapter 6, page 230)

Mode of Entry	Critical Success Factor
1. Exporting	Existence of tariffs and quotas
2. Licensing	Appropriability of intellectual property
3. Franchising	Quality control of franchisee
4. Contract manufacturing	Reliability and quality of local contractor
5. Service sector outsourcing	Impact on supply chain costs
6. Turnkey operations	Reliable infrastructure
7. Joint ventures	Strategic fit of partner
8. Wholly owned subsidiary	Repatriability of profits

b) List the advantages of international joint ventures compared with fully-owned subsidiaries, and list the advantages of fully-owned subsidiaries over IJVs. Organize your out your answer as "IJV Advantages" and "Fully-Owned Subsidiary Advantages." (Chapter 6, page 230)

IJV Advantages	Fully-Owned Subsidiary Advantages
Insider access to markets	Insider access to markets
Share costs (and profits) with partner	Appropriate all revenues
Leverage partner's skill base	Protect technology and skill base
Share risks (and control) with partner	Exercise total control over operation
Leverage partner's local contacts	Experience global economies of scale

3. **You are considering a joint venture in Russia between your U.S. firm and a Russian firm:**

   a) List five of the problems you anticipate with the IJV in Russia, along with the possible solutions/ways to minimize the risk of each of those problems. Organize your answer as "Problems" and "Solutions."
   (Chapter 7, pages 248-250)

Problems	Solutions
1. Possible nationalization of assets	OPIC (Overseas Private Investment Insurance). Have JV partner work on relationships with government authorities.
2. Corruption and bribe-taking at all levels of state bureaucracy	Have JV partner help with negotiating with state bureaucracy. Paying certain bribes is illegal under U.S. law (Foreign Corrupt Practice Act, FCPA). Communicate early and up front that your company does not pay bribes.
3. Weak legislative and enforcement regimes	Have Russian JV partner work on relationships as the means of getting things done. Set up meetings with local ministries and regional authorities.
4. Poor quality raw material and supplies	Vertical integration

   b) From your article readings, give an update on the changing business climate in Russia.

   The instructor may require the students write an update of the business climate in Russia as it relates to IJVs and present their findings in this answer. The update should address the problems above (for example, have there been any changes corruption and bribe-taking?) as well address any new problems not discussed in the Comparative Management in Focus in Chapter 7.

4. **a) Name and explain the two types (extremes) of strategic choice as an overall strategic approach to world markets for firms which operate around the world, discussing their comparative advantages, and give an example of a product or service for each choice.**
(Chapter 6, pages 219-222)

The two basic strategic choices available to MNC in their approach to world markets are globalization and regionalization. Globalization refers to strategies that treat the world as an undifferentiated world wide marketplace. This leads firms to integrate their activities on a world wide basis to capture the linkages among countries. The advantages accrued by following this strategy are reaping benefits of worldwide economies of scale, offshore manufacturing, and international cash flows. Industrial products such as earth-moving equipment like that manufactured by Caterpillar, or certain household appliances like Sony TVs have fared well with global strategies.

The regionalization strategy is one in which local markets are linked together within a region, allowing more local responsiveness and specialization. Top managers within each region decide on their own investment locations, product-mixes, and competitive positioning thus allowing for flexibility and adaptability to local conditions. The advantages of the regionalization strategies lie in being able to cater to unique consumer preferences resulting from cultural differences, availing of or countering domestic subsidies, and using new technologies that allow variation with little additional cost. A regionalization strategy also exposes the company to less environmental risk. British retailer Tesco is an example of a firm that has succeeded using a regionalization strategy in South Korea. Samsung Tesco is 89% British owned by the British giant, but has relied heavily on local managers from Samsung. Matsushita is another example. In Malaysia, it tries to keep the expatriate headcount down and train local managers. It also tailors products to markets and lets plants set their own rules.

b) Explain the appropriate structural elements necessary to implement each of the two strategies in a) above. (Chapter 8, pages 267-270)

The organization structure will follow the strategic choice that is made whether it is globalization or regionalization. Since most companies follow a mixture of both strategies i.e., they fall somewhere on the continuum between the two extreme choices of globalization (treating all markets as one) and regionalization (treating every market as individual).

The most common choice of structure is the global geographic structure where country and regional needs and relative market knowledge take precedence over product expertise. Companies that are heavily into consumer products with a focus on marketing such as Nestle, and Unilever generally follow this structure. On the other hand, a complete globalization strategy could conceivably be achieved through a global functional or a global product structure.

Increasingly though, the future of MNCs in terms of organization structure seems to lie in a network structure that is characterized by relational networks which lie on the centralization-decentralization continuum balancing the tension between differentiation and integration.

Exam 3: Chapters 9-11

Answer all of the four questions (5 points each). Lay out your answers using numbers, letters, or bullet format as necessary.

Be sure to give full, comprehensive answers with enough detail to convince the reader that you understand the concepts. Be sure that your answer demonstrates knowledge and understanding of the course and text. Use subheadings and bulleted lists as appropriate.

1. **a) Compare the advantages of the ethnocentric, polycentric, and global approaches to staffing international operations.** (Chapter 9, pages 343-345)

    Advantages of the ethnocentric staffing approach: PCNs are familiar with company goals, products, technology policies and procedures and they know how to get things done through the company headquarters. PCNs also tend to be more loyal to the company than are local managers.

    Advantages of the Polycentric staffing approach: HCNs are more familiar with local conditions and culture and know the local ways of doing business. They have important contacts and are more likely to be accepted by people inside and outside the organization. In terms of cost, they will cost much less to hire than PCNs.

    Advantages of the global staffing approach: This approach provides a greater pool of qualified and willing candidates to choose from. It also results a culturally adept and more flexible global management cadre who may have bilingual or multi-lingual skills. It may also be more cost effective to use transpatriates instead of expatriates.

    b) What are the factors that will affect your choice of staffing?
    (Chapter 9, pages. 343-345)

    Ethnocentric Staffing Approach (PCN): Cost of salary and benefits, "hardship package", level of technical capability required, close contact with head office required as in the initial stages of set up, would be factors that will influence selection of ethnocentric staffing approach.

    Polycentric Staffing Approach (HCN): How much local customs and culture matter in the product or industry, whether local government requirements have to be met, whether there is availability of skilled labor force in the country, and whether autonomy can be granted from head office-are all factors to be considered in selection of the polycentric staffing approach.

Global Staffing Approach (TCN): Availability of skilled personnel, high level of flexibility and cultural adaptability is required and the whether best person irrespective of nationality needs to be chosen, are factors to be considered in the selection of global staffing approach.

2. **List five of the primary reasons for expatriate failure, along with solutions for each to increase the likelihood of success of the expatriate's assignment:** (Chapter 9, pages 348-349)

Reason for Expatriate failure	Solution
1. Inadequate preparation, training, and orientation prior to assignment	Extensive preparation and training for cross-cultural interactions is critical. Area studies, culture assimilators, language and sensitivity training and field experiences are all required
2. Alienation and lack of support from headquarters	Keeping in constant touch with expatriate and providing support
3. Problems with spouse and children-family adjustment problems	Consult and interview spouse before assignment Let spouse initiate own training program Provide language and culture training to spouse and family
4. Insufficient compensation and financial support	Use balance sheet approach for compensation Keep expatriate "whole"
5. Poor programs for career support and repatriation	Have a long range career plan for executive, such that he knows even before he leaves where he is likely to be posted upon return. Provide ongoing support to expatriate while he is on assignment abroad.

3. **Discuss Germany's labor relations system, including the "codetermination" law, and the role of works councils. What are the implications for firms such as DaimlerChrysler, A.G.? What effect is globalization having on codetermination?** (Chapter 10, page 390-391)

Germany's codetermination law (*mitbestimmung*)—which refers to the participation of labor in the management of a firm—mandates representation for unions and salaried employees on the supervisory boards of all large companies and "works councils" of employees at every work site. Unions are well integrated into managerial decision-making and can make a positive contribution to corporate competitiveness and restructuring.

Union membership in Germany is voluntary, usually with one union for each major industry, and union power is quite strong. Negotiated contracts with firms by the employers' federation stand to be accepted by firms who are members of the federation, or used as a guide for other firms. These contracts, therefore, result in setting the pay scale for about 90 percent of the country's workers. The union works councils play an active role in hiring, firing, and reassignment during times of reorganization and change.

Codetermination has clearly helped modify the German managerial style, from authoritarian to something more akin to humanitarian, without altering its capacity for efficiency and effectiveness. This system compares to the lack of integration and active roles for unions in the U.S. auto industry, for example, conditions that limit opportunities for change.

DaimlerChrysler, the German-American company headquartered in Germany, includes a works council in its decision-making, as mandated by German law. This means that the company's labor representatives pay close attention to U.S. attitudes, which may lead to changes in the tone of the collective bargaining processes. The two-tiered system of a supervisory and a management board remains. DaimlerChrysler was one of several companies to exert pressure in 2004 to bring down the high labor costs and taxes in Germany, under the threat of moving its plants elsewhere to remain globally competitive.

Pay for German production workers has been among the highest in the world, about 150 percent of that in the United States and about ten times that in Mexico. German workers also have the highest number of paid vacation days in the world and prefer short workdays. In July 2004, however, Jurgen Peters, chairman of Germany's powerful IG Metall engineering trade union, announced the agreement with DaimlerChrysler to accept smaller raises and increased working hours, after the company threatened to move 6,000 jobs elsewhere.

The codetermination law is, however, coming under pressure as a result of globalization. German firms, in order to remain more competitive against foreign firms, need unions to make more concessions. Under pressure from globalization, German unions have incurred large membership losses. As a result, they are now more willing to make concessions. For example, the German firm Linde decided to build a factory in Eastern Europe to take advantage of lower wages. Linde reversed the decision, however, after the IG Metall trade union decided to match the savings by working longer hours and taking less pay.

4. **Describe the prevailing motivational climate in Eastern Europe with special reference to Russia. As part of your answer, discuss the conflicting motivational techniques used by Western vs. Russian managers with Russian employees.** (Chapter 11, page 409)

Western firms entering Eastern European markets should realize that workers are accustomed to working under very different circumstances and being motivated in different ways. Specific examples (based on Russia) are found in a study by Michailova. This study found that:

- Russian employees are still used to a management style that prevailed in a centrally planned economic system
- The centrally planned system resulted in vertical hierarchies and little individualism
- Employees were more motivated by authoritarianism of their Russian managers than by empowerment by Western managers

Some conflicting motivational techniques found by Michailova are given below:

Western managers told their Russian employees to:

- Take the initiative and give suggestions
- Learn from mistakes and don't repeat them
- Look longer term and to the future
- Think of the company as an integrated entity

Russian managers told their Russian employees:

- Obey the rules: just do what you are supposed to do
- Mistakes are not allowed and will be punished
- Concentrate on the here and now
- Act according to your job description and don't be concerned about other people's jobs